Elroy Bode's
TEXAS SKETCHBOOK

A Sheaf of Prose Poems

Introduction by
MILTON LEECH

Drawings by
JOSE CISNEROS

TEXAS WESTERN PRESS
THE UNIVERSITY OF TEXAS AT EL PASO

RO1 0101 2115

COPYRIGHT 1967

THE UNIVERSITY OF TEXAS AT EL PASO

Library of Congress Catalog Card No. 67-29808

Edited by

MILTON LEECH

and

S. D. MYRES

Typographic Arrangement by
CARL HERTZOG

71B 2660

INTRODUCTION

By Milton Leech

"When i began to read an author, I very soon caught the tune of the song beneath the words, which in each author is distinct from that of every other." Marcel Proust knew what most of us feel when he made this observation in On Art and Literature. A cursory glance or a third reading of the sketches which follow will reveal the tune of the song beneath the author's words. This kind of creative writing has not received major attention by the Texas Western Press until now, but the quality of Elroy Bode's word pictures is so evident that the publishing of this collection seems a necessity.

The material is arranged geographically — according to areas around Texas — but the book need not be read from page one to the end to be enjoyable. A casual glance at some particular passage or the re-reading of a well-phrased sentence can be just as pleasant.

We do not hesitate to believe that what Bode says is true. He has an involvement with the people, places, and moods of El Paso, Juárez, the hill country, the Gulf coast, and scattered parts of Texas. This involvement produces the magic ingredient of empathy: reader and author are communicating closely with each other. The communicative aspects found here — the giving by the author and the receiving by the reader — are often completed when the reader's reaction takes place, but it is the remembering of these reactions that will take many readers back to favorite passages for repeated pleasure. The Sketches have a simplicity and lucidity entirely free from affectation; they are straightforward and vivid, with occasional social comments. Bode seems to have Whitman's affection for all that is homely and of the soil. We experience a personal intimacy with his characters.

In "Sunday Morning at Canutillo" he speaks about "a feast for the senses," a theme which runs throughout many of the sketches. He appeals to our senses when he describes Mrs. Bergman tasting dirt in her vegetable garden; when he tells about the smell of campfire smoke; and when he pictures Gram repeatedly running her thumb across her fingers.

Animal life is used throughout the collection as still another theme. Animals appear both as subjects for sketches and as minor characters. We meet a pet lamb, an old buck sheep, a rabbit at sundown, long-legged birds, as well as the dogs that are so essential to ranch life in the hill country.

In Bode's pursuit of these themes and of all the others, poetic qualities are dominant. It is probably a combination of prose and poetry that brings together a series of seemingly unrelated subjects in such a way that they create a single impact. The author's emotional range is wide enough to extend from his evident delight with life itself to the tenderness and pathos found in "Enselmo and the Triplets," but this range is a clear indication that human nature with all of its complex facets is something that Bode understands. His agreeable prose poems are a welcome shower of honesty in contrast with the poetic cloudburst of often unintelligible word arrangements from many contemporary writers. At a time when *so much that is being written is obscure and gloomy, the freshness and clarity of these vignettes is to be relished. One test of their quality is that they do not actually need an explanation.*

Elroy Bode was born in Kerrville, Texas, in 1931. He attended The University of Texas at Austin where he was a member of Phi Beta Kappa. He graduated summa cum laude with Bachelor of Arts and Bachelor of Science degrees in 1954; he served two years in the United States Air Force as a lieutenant and for the past ten years has been a teacher in the public schools of Texas. Since 1960, his stories and sketches have been published in the Texas Observer, Southwest Review, *Texas Quarterly, Descant, New Mexico Quarterly, Southwesterner, South Dakota Review, and* Redbook. *He has had an article accepted for inclusion in the forthcoming (Spring, 1967) anthology,* Best American Magazine Articles *in 1967.*

CONTENTS

CONTENTS

I

On the Border: El Paso

Spring in the Plaza

W IN MARCH, when the mornings begin to lose their chill and the elm trees begin to bud, the downtown plaza in El Paso ceases to be the bleak, wind-swept bus stop of wintertime and once again resumes its rightful character as the heart of the city.

The first of the religious orators take up their positions near the center alligator pond — usually in pairs, one speaking in English, the other following in Spanish. Both revolve slowly, arms outstretched, facing little groups of onlookers who watch them as they would a fist fight or the attack of an epileptic — with the same detached curiosity.

Old men in mismatched clothes — the regular park idlers, the swappers of tales about ailments and travels and philosophies — are joined by secretaries and business men taking a few moments from lunch hours and coffee breaks; by college students, soldiers, and tourists; by school children on their way home; by maids waiting for their bus; by all the downtown strollers who wander through to watch the people and take a look at the alligator and in general keep up with what's going on.

The alligator crawls out of the cold, blue-tinted water and lies on the gravel pathway, his chin resting on the edge of the pool. Cigarette butts, small rocks, matches — such things soon accumulate on his back, thrown by bored and idle young men who would like to see the alligator awaken from his torpor and amuse them with a yawning display of jaws.

Off to one side of the plaza a small hunchbacked man in a double-breasted blue suit and with severely-parted, smooth black hair talks to a group of men — explaining Marx's theory, the life of Mary Baker Eddy: who knows? But he is very articulate and evidently quite persuasive. The men listen to him gravely, nodding in agreement now and then — as though just on the verge of professing Judaism or agreeing to some new labor-management arbitration.

Thin little Mexican women — who have probably spent more time walking than most people have spent sitting — come briskly into the plaza from the north, make the half-circle detour around the alligator pond, and pass on to the south toward the *tranvia* stop and Juárez: looking neither right nor left and never slowing down, the knotted calf muscles in their wiry legs flexing with each step like small mechanical instruments constantly changing gear (while at the same moment their younger, prettier sisters — girls with hair-dos like great fluffy clumps of black cotton candy — loiter through numerous slow circles around the alligator pond: laughing, slapping one another's shoulders and arms in artificial glee as they let themselves be consumed by the eyes of lounging, match-chewing young men).

And all the while — as the alligator sleeps and the strollers amble and the old men sit with their feet wide apart telling how it was in Guatemala in the '30s — there is contentment in the air. It is as if peaceful alliances have finally been reached between the forces of nature. Morning passes on into afternoon and no discordant note jangles the air — the pigeons coast and wheel above the grass, the flag waves imperially from its small granite monument, and the buildings on surrounding streets continue to jut up in pleasant alternations with cloudless blue sky. ≳

Old Men in the Library

✦ EACH TIME it is a shock. At five minutes after nine each morning, when you have just had your third cup of coffee and second cigarette and are still feeling that the world is only a few minutes past daybreak, you walk woodenly into the El Paso public library and down the stairs into the basement periodical room and find them already sitting there — a whole roomful of silent gray-haired men half hidden behind newspapers. The library doesn't open until nine, yet within five minutes they have got the *Denver Post* and the *Christian Science Monitor* and the *Chicago Tribune* off the rack and have settled in their straight-backed chairs to read — some with magnifying glasses, some with a senile trembling of the pages, some with a constant labored movement

of their lips. Most of the papers are at least a day or two old, but that doesn't seem to matter. To these men — the blue coat, brown pants, yellow tie crowd — it's the sense of morning ritual that counts. They just like to sit in the chairs with their newspapers spread before them: it helps them feel involved with the world, a little more in touch (and with the metal binding rods stuck through the spine of the papers and angled out jauntily almost like guidons or lances, they manage to achieve a kind of quiet, fraternal decorum — as if they are retired British colonels scanning the *Manchester Guardian* in their oak-paneled club).

By nine-thirty most of the men get what they want from the newspapers and branch out to magazines. They begin a hobbling and shuffling transit from their chairs to the racks, first picking up a copy of *Holiday* and thumbing through its colorful pages, then replacing it for something solid-looking like *US News and World Report*. They are great eclectics, willing to spend a few minutes on almost anything that is printed: *Audubon Magazine, American Journal of Public Health, Leatherneck, UNESCO Courier*. Sometimes they read the text, sometimes they look at pictures, but mostly they just thumb idly through the pages.

Most of the early wave is ready to leave by ten o'clock — their essential rootlessness finally driving them back into the streets. A few will linger a while along the racks, lifting up a magazine, staring at the cover picture inside its plastic jacket, letting it slip down again onto the wire. But soon they, too, become jaded with the heavy silence of the room. They look at their watches and gaze vacantly at the newcomers who have drifted in and are settled comfortably in their reading — then scowling to themselves and bobbing their heads like old slow horses going out to pasture, they move past the desk where they laid their hats and disappear upstairs into the street.

Geisha Rockefeller

✻ THE PINK ELEPHANT LOUNGE in downtown El Paso is a bar where GI's and the college crowd play miniature bowling and try to pick up dates. It was managed for a while by a pretty Japanese woman with a rosebud mouth and an adding machine for a brain. I never knew what her real name was, but someone had aptly dubbed her Geisha Rockefeller.

She was the wife of the owner — an elegant little sample of Tokyo nightlife acquired when he was off soldiering. The owner himself was a mild, slightly balding man in his thirties who had several bars around town and only dropped in occasionally at the Pink Elephant. He would saunter in and talk a while to the big-bellied guard at the door, then to Geisha, and generally end up having a number of long beers with buddies of his at the back of the bar. Regardless of how long he stayed or how busy things got, he left the managing strictly to Geisha.

There was never any doubt who was boss. Whether she was merely perched up on a bar stool, or playing a quick game of miniature bowling with a customer, or pointing a waitress toward an empty table that needed clearing, Geisha commanded the bar as efficiently as any drill sergeant deploying troops on a parade ground (and just as there would be familiar, comfortable sounds to the sergeant — the unisoned tramping of many feet, the shouted cadences — there were noises in the Pink Elephant which obviously pleased Geisha: the constant ringing of the cash register, the laughter from the booths and tables, the crashes of the miniature bowling game).

She was quite a concentrated little eyeful and of course was the big drawing card for the lounge. Cool and confident as all get out, beautifully lipped and haired and cheek-boned, she was always dressed in tight-fitting knit dresses that

swelled and coasted their way down her small graceful
curves. As she sat motionless at the end of the counter and
surveyed the goings-on in the lounge — her hands resting on
her thighs, her arm bracelets slipped down about her wrists,
one high-heeled leg and foot drawn back toward the counter
a fraction — she was a classic Oriental doll and there was no
idle male who did not find himself staring at the exquisite
perfection of her body. And even when she bowled (never
bothering to watch the ball hit the pins: just moving automatically with her quick little bend, arm thrust, and recovery
so she would have time to sweep a glance around the bar
before repeating her routine again), she was still a doll-in-
motion, a story-book face and figure that kept increasing its
exotic allure in the neon-lit darkness.

Of the many times I sat in the lounge only once did I see
Geisha display her dollar consciousness to the point that she
lost composure. I was seated near her at the counter one
night when one of the waitresses — a dreary blonde girl with
a pointed chin — started bawling out a soldier in a booth.
"Watch her," the fellow next to me said, nodding toward
Geisha. "She's not about to lose that guy. He's been sopping
it up in here since four this afternoon." When I turned to
look at Geisha she was already down from her stool and
headed toward the booth. She started off just fine, with her
characteristic ball-bearing grace, but half-way there her poise
deserted her completely and she became just one more short-
legged business woman hurrying over to soothe a customer.
Her elbows began working a little too much and at too wide
an angle; her hips broke into an awkward duck-like waddle.
For a moment she could easily have been a midget wrestler
headed toward the ring.

She gave the waitress several minutes of solid, high-pitched
hell, refusing to listen as the girl explained that for the third
time that night the soldier had spilled beer on her dress. The

soldier, who had been drunkenly loud to the skinny waitress, began to quieten obediently as Geisha laid an easy, familiar hand on his shoulder and talked to him and his three friends. There were promises of better behavior — the soldier nodding a great deal and even trying to get up and bow to Geisha as she left. The waitress came back to the counter, her apron and dress wet and her eyes blinking back tears. She ordered another beer for the soldier and then sniffled her way back toward the rest rooms.

When Geisha returned to her stool she was completely unruffled, in full command of herself and the bar. She smiled at the bright remarks of the college boys nearby, her mouth pursed charmingly into noncommittal and unspoken replies. She smoothed her dress across her waist and sculptured little thighs. And out of the corners of her shrewdly slitted eyes she began playing the old familiar game: watching the customers as they watched her. It was all very much business-as-usual again in the Pink Elephant.

Irmalinda

IRMALINDA STEALS, and I will have to let her go. But I cannot say to her, "Irmalinda, you steal" — just like that. First of all, I have never caught her taking anything; I have no proof. Things are simply missing from the house — a little money, a few towels, my wife's hairpins, a couple of diapers. They are all small things, things that would fit easily into Irmalinda's purse when she leaves each afternoon and returns to Juárez.

It is the principle, of course — you don't want to have a maid you can't trust. She will just keep on taking things until you can't afford to ignore it. And besides, if she steals, perhaps she isn't to be trusted with the baby. You just can't tell. . . .

"Irmalinda, there is something I must tell you. You are stealing from us; therefore I must let you go" — is that how to do it: abruptly, the Master of the House informing the Pilfering Servant Girl she must leave? I would be perfectly within my rights. I have no proof, true, but things are definitely missing — and it is a situation which can only grow worse. How could I possibly keep on calmly greeting her each day, saying, "Good morning, Irmalinda; is it very cold out?" and then wondering what she was going to carry away in the afternoon — a comb, perhaps, or a pair of my wife's earrings, or one of the baby's dresses?

Yet I keep saying to myself: maybe I ought to drop this righteous attitude. For I have been to Juárez. I know how the people are forced to live there. I have walked those streets and seen the old women scavenging in garbage cans; I have seen the poverty and have felt the pangs of guilt at my having so much when they have so little. And I have read enough and seen enough to realize that morality is generally no more than a point of view: I, the white Protestant college graduate living in my air-conditioned house, can look upon life with a purity and idealism that a colored man in Mississippi or a Mexican in Juárez does not share (steal? rob a supermarket? Ah, no, the moral one says; I would not. Or is it only that I *need* not?)

All right, I say: what if I simply accept the fact that a few pins, a diaper here and there, twenty cents bus fare twice a week are things I can well afford to lose to my little splintery-legged Irmalinda. Aren't they small contributions indeed to a sixteen-year-old girl whose mother not only works but is pregnant again as well — a girl with seven smaller sisters at home ready to join the Juárez labor force whenever they can get their permits? Isn't life hard enough, unfair enough, to someone like Irmalinda — who should still be in school instead of washing clothes and sweeping floors — without my having to play the role of the godly American *patrón?*

Yet — and my inner dialogue turns still another corner: doesn't she actually expect to get caught? When she works up to canned goods and silverware — as undoubtedly she will if I let her — how can she hope not to be confronted one day and asked to leave? Even as young as she is, isn't she simply being fatalistic, knowing she has to take whatever she can before the inevitable dismissal?

I pursue my questions, and can only come to one sad conclusion: I will have to let her go. Despite knowing that Irmalinda, like the underprivileged everywhere, simply regards stealing as one of the weapons of the Have Nots in their long silent war with the Haves, I must hold her accountable. To understand why she steals does not excuse me from doing what I think is right.

Somehow, though I'm not sure why, I have the feeling that Irmalinda will take her dismissal perfectly in stride — with a slight shrug and a nod and an "All right, sir, if that is your wish." She will gather her few personal things out of the closet and then, smiling one last childish but already professional smile, she will leave the house, closing the door firmly and quietly behind her and walking with her bare, lonely Mexican dignity down the street toward the bus stop. ⧨

Milady

❧ I SAW A WOMAN in a parking lot — a very slim and fashionably dressed woman — and for a long moment just the sight of her caused me to balance between outrage and a kind of giddy despair. Not that she and her midday elegance were at all outrageous in themselves: it was just that such a chic dash of noon-time femininity, such a pretty little human frill, juxtaposed itself too sharply, too incongruously, against past scenes of the morning.

For I had left behind, in south El Paso, other women—those in the alleys and doorways and patios of dirty red-brick apartment houses: women with dark roomsful of children, women bent over washing clothes, women carrying heavy bundles, women with babies on their hips staring out through screened doorways. There was no sign of elegance there — only the cheerless concerns of people fighting the daily battles of poverty and survival.

To leave those women and walk north toward the business district just in time to see Milady get out of her small foreign car — to see so slim and twisty-tailed a trick emerge like a butterfly from the shiny red cocoon of her Jaguar — made me lose all perspective about life and human nature. My first impulse was simply to shout at the woman: Lady, how can you — how *dare* you — exist in such splendid isolation from your sister humans? How can you be so oblivious of the lives they lead, their constant burdens? Who are you to be exempt from rub-boards and hungry bellies?

But my quixotic indignation gradually melted and I realized there was nothing to be gained by being upset. Indeed, asking such a woman to be concerned about social injustices and inequalities would be like asking a peacock to give up its feathers to make pillows for the Salvation Army. So I withdrew my demands of her and just watched, for she made an undeniably pretty sight moving along with her small rapid steps toward the Citizens' National Bank. With one black-gloved hand she would touch, automatically and very lightly, her stunning little rear to check the smoothness of her beautifully tailored yellow dress (— a wholly useless gesture; the dress, as she well knew, hugged her slim hips like a silky banana skin). And with the other gloved hand reaching up to her hat — a tall upside-down felt chamberpot with white brim and bow — and constantly glancing about little-girlishly through her dark glasses, she let the small arcs of her shiny black shoes carry her through the side entrance of the bank.

There she is, I thought, the slim society matron going about the routines of her nicely appointed day: a pop-in at the bank, a green-salad lunch with similarly sheathed and bedecked young friends, a shopping tour through the best department stores followed by an executive meeting of the Garden Club. Considering her, I couldn't help wondering: Did she inhabit the same earth and breathe the same air as the women of south El Paso? Was she truly their human kin, or of an entirely different species? Would the camel pass through the needle's eye before Milady of the Parking Lot understood that life was more than a tall, but very dry, martini?

Mexican Families

W I DON'T WANT TO BE FOOLISH or naive about this, but sometimes I think that Mexican families get along better than other families — at least, they seem able to take life in stride and come up with some daily satisfactions.

Take the family across the street from where I live. They have a coupé with a sun visor and white sidewalls parked in their driveway. Now, personally, I go for a different kind of car, but I can easily understand how a family would like that coupé – would like to have it sitting washed and shiny in front of the house. It would be something to be proud of and take nice rides in on Sunday afternoon.

Take their yard. It is extremely small, just big enough to have two squares of yellowed grass on either side of the walk, a few cannas, a couple of tall salt cedars. But look at that small boy playing in it: he seems to get along quite well. He can dig in it, can mess it up some of he wants because he knows that his front yard is not an inviolate showplace, a place only for visitors.

Take the young husband. He is out on the front porch now, nailing something – a chair, cabinets maybe. There is mariachi music coming onto the porch from the living room, and while the husband nails he listens to the music and sings along with it, occasionally even adding a little shrill whistling. There is also a slim and very pleasant-looking brown-and-white dog walking casually about on the porch – quite content, looking as if he, too, might break out with an exuberant Mexican *grito* if he decides his voice is in shape.

Inside the house the hands of the young wife can be seen behind one of the window screens, cleaning. White curtains keep flowing against her hands – almost fondly, as if trying to volunteer their help and guidance.

The house itself is a small one, made of red brick with a typically old-fashioned four-sided roof fitting on top like a kind of awkward dunce cap. Since it is not yet spring there are withered vines running up the porch, and three small elms along the sidewalk still remain bare.

And though it is not a particularly uplifting scene, perhaps, nothing about the house or the yard or the people is winter-sad. Yet I have seen many such houses that are – unless

Mexicans are living there. The Anglo man who stands on his lawn after work, reaching down to get the afternoon paper and then staring out at cars passing in the street — he always seems a little bitter, the kind to go in and drink his beer at the kitchen table and quarrel all through supper with the children and his wife. The children themselves who play out on the front porch in the dim rays of the February sun — they seem almost forlorn: private, isolated, out-of-touch. And even sounds coming from within the house — dishes rattling, closet doors shutting: they seem like brief, depressing commentaries on the loneliness of life.

I truly have no ax to grind in this; I have nothing to gain. It just seems to me that Mexicans generally act as though the house they live in is — for better or for worse — their home, while others, in the same type of house, in the same limited economic circumstances, manage to appear like graceless captives in an alien land.

The French Couple

ON SUNDAY MORNINGS the young French soldier and his wife got off the bus from Fort Bliss and walked slowly up the plaza sidewalk hand in hand. When they reached the alligator pond the wife always took a little hop and sat on the wall a split second before her husband moved to help her (you could do that: sit there on top of the low green wall and swing your legs and watch the people strolling by). The girl was small and very pretty, her face like the enlarged drawing of a smiling milkmaid lifted from some child's storybook. She always wore a silk scarf pulled tightly across her head and then pushed back just far enough to leave a rim of light-brown hair showing in front.

Her knitted red sweater was a little too bulky but it made her look nicely casual — comrade-like, as if she and her husband were taking a walk across the Pyrenees and had merely stopped to rest in a village square. The sweater was constantly sliding down her arms and she was always mechanically pushing the sleeves back up to her elbows by rubbing her arm against her hip bone. Many times when the sleeves began to slip the husband would reach over with curved palms and guide them carefully back into place. Sometimes she wore blue Japanese sandals and white toreador pants. The pants were never tight-fitting; they did not shout at you, "See my shapely legs and nice behind!" They were loose and neat and pressed — just the kind that would please a jealous and protective husband.

Each Sunday for a month the couple spent their time in the plaza that way — the girl sitting on the wall, the husband standing rather tense and formal at her side. Whenever the girl spotted someone that delighted her fancy, she would lean over — without quite taking her eyes from the passerby — and

whisper deeply into her husband's ear. Then she would pull
herself straight, her hands still tightly gripping the rim of the
wall, and smile down at her husband while he turned stiffly
to look at the person too. He never bothered to look very long.
He would give a single obligatory glance, smile vaguely, then
turn back aggressively — as if half-expecting to find that during the brief interim of looking someone had jumped up on
the wall beside his wife and had begun to make advances.

The husband was a swarthy, serious-faced man with heavy
black eyebrows, a short bull neck, and big handsome teeth.
His dark hair was cut in the European style: closely clipped
high above the ears, then allowed to spread out in a thick mop.
(Sometimes, perhaps out of nervousness or merely to comb
his hair, he would cup his hands together and draw back
quickly across his head). He tried his best to smile and be
pleasant — to appear interested in whatever his wife found
to whisper about — but it was obviously a strain. Being alert
to his wife's every movement and need was a serious, full-
time business: he simply had no time to waste on anything
else.

And sitting on the wall was something he could not do very
successfully either. His wife kept inviting him to join her, and

to please her he would try it for a while. But soon — as though by reflex — he would jump down and begin walking in front of her in his restrained little circle, always keeping one hand firmly on the wall beside her thigh. ·

The last Sunday that the couple came to the plaza a blond-haired young man sat down on the wall beside the French girl. He did not speak to her; he just hopped up, pulled out a cigarette from his shirt pocket, and began to tap it on the top of the wall. He had put the cigarette to his lips and was searching in his pants pocket for a lighter when the French soldier stepped across in front of his wife and said, "Please — do not sit there."

The young man's mouth opened slightly, the cigarette angling downward. "Why the hell not?" he said. "Just look around. Ever'body sits up here." The young man fixed what he probably considered to be a steady eye on the husband, then continued to feel around in his pockets for the lighter.

The French soldier pointed along the wall and out toward the benches underneath the elm trees. "Yes, other place . . . many places. But here, sir, no. . . ."

The blond young man drew out the lighter from his back pocket. "I don't know what's troublin' you, buddy, but you better not press your luck. It's a free country. . . . I'm not doin' nothin' to your girl friend here." And after a quick glance side-wise at the French girl he bent his head forward to light his cigarette — as though the matter was closed.

The flame of his lighter was still an inch away from the Marlboro when the French soldier placed one hand against the young man's chest and sent him toppling backwards onto the border of grass inside the alligator pond. The young man hit hard, on his shoulder, but he was on his feet quickly.

"Goddam you," he said, his blond face flushing red," "god-dam you."

The soldier stood on the other side of the wall, his fists tightened, a big corded vein pulsing in his neck. People nearby were watching now, and a few had begun to move in a little closer.

But the young man didn't fight. As he was putting his hands to the inside ledge of the wall, the French girl, who had jumped down to stand beside her husband, moved toward him and said, "Please, sir, my husband . . . it is hard to tell you; my husband loves me . . . I am his wife."

The young man, who was as tall as the soldier but not as muscular, stared out at the girl from the alligator pond.

"Well, hell, all I was doing was *sittin'* here. *Christ!*" And with grass stuck to his shirt and neck and hair he stood for a moment glaring at the girl who was smiling now with her beautiful, red-ringed smile. Then he vaulted back over the wall as athletically as he could and began brushing himself off. The soldier, who had picked up the young man's cigarette lighter, presented it to him, and after the young man took it the soldier formally offered his hand. But the young man would not shake. He gave a shrug and walked away — scowling, pretending to be wholly preoccupied with searching through his pockets for his pack of cigarettes.

Most of the crowd that had pressed in toward the wall began to break up and move back toward the benches, disappointed in the lack of violence. A few lingered, watching as the French girl put her hand on her husband's arm and spoke to him. They saw the soldier nod, touch his wife lightly at the waist, and then, stepping to one side, follow behind her as they walked down the plaza sidewalk toward the bus stop. The girl was smiling pleasantly and the soldier was solemn and alert.

Music

W I HAD SEEN HIM AROUND for several months, rocking
along the streets in the same tired, relentless way — usually
crossing in front of a Rexall drugstore as I drove toward the
center of town. It would be about one-thirty in the afternoon
and, as I paused at the traffic light, here he would come,
walking like a pudgy human metronome with bunions. He
moved as steadily from side to side as he did straight ahead,
as if resisting his own progress every step of the way. He always appeared to be in the grip of a huge indifference or
sadness, as though neither the hot sun above, nor the cars
and people passing by — nothing in the whole world around
him — was of any consequence. With his shoulders drooping
and his hands flopping loosely at his side, he seemed to be
using his body to express a deep philosophic "Ho-Hum."

He seldom varied his dress. Generally he wore a pair of
blue denims several sizes too large and cinched in tight across
his middle by an old black belt; a denim shirt with the sleeves
hacked off at each shoulder; and tennis shoes. Sometimes he
had on a white sailor's cap with the brim turned down, or else
a grey woolen tam o'shanter. As he passed my car he looked
like a gloomy and bleary-eyed Irishman who had finally become disenchanted with the British navy: who had jumped
ship at Vera Cruz and then made his way — casually, unhur-
riedly — across Mexico.

I did not see him for a while — had even forgot to look for
his strange, head-bobbing figure to cross in front of my car —
and then one afternoon on my way to town I stopped at the
drugstore for a sandwich and a cup of coffee. I was seated
at the counter, reading a newspaper and nursing the coffee
along, when I saw him slouch through the door. He was

dressed the same as always, and as he circled behind a couple of women near the cash register I wondered if he felt embarrassed about how he looked — a beachcomber in a medical building drugstore. But he moved on past the customers without seeming to give them or the drugstore any special concern, so I assumed they didn't bother him. He went to the cigar counter, gazed at it for a while, then slid back one of the glass doors and picked out a Tampa Nugget.

Well, all right, I thought — so much for all this. He is simply a man who dresses the way he wants to and wanders aimlessly about town like a lot of others do: just another loner, another homeless middle-aged man with a little bit of the stuffing kicked out of him by life. But he'll buy his cigar and smoke it on the remainder of his rounds and maybe it will stir up memories of good, by-gone places — Malaya, Port of Spain, County Cork. . . .

There were several other customers ready to pay their checks now and they began to join the man near the cash register. But even though his cigar was in his hand and he was obviously the next to pay, the man stepped back to the end of the line and took up a position beside the candy counter. Since he looked at no one — avoided any direct contact of eyes — I thought perhaps I had been wrong: that maybe he really was self-conscious about his appearance and simply used indifference as a pose.

I went back to my coffee and sandwich, satisfied in knowing, more or less, what the man would do: first, he would let everyone else clear out of the store. Then, stepping up to the cash register, he would search about nonchalantly in his deep pants for the change. Finally — to the further irritation of the rather prim middle-aged lady cashier — he would pause a while to light up and experimentally puff his cigar before ambling on out the door.

In a moment, however, I quickly looked up, for the man had started to hum — not loud enough to disturb anyone, just with enough force that I could hear him above the small, scattered noises of the drugstore. I assumed that this, too, was merely a part of the man's waiting routine — that he found it pleasant to strike up an idle melody or two as he waited patiently in the background. And I immediately liked the man a little more for doing that, for saying to himself: "Ahh, let the check-clutchers hurry by; I'll stand here and hum me a little tune before I'll break me blasted *neck.*"

But the customers left and still the man did not go to the cash register; he remained in front of the candy stand and kept on humming. With one wrist grasped firmly by the other hand — rather formally, as if he were onstage performing for an audience — he stood there, comfortably erect, his head moving up and down in a controlled but very pronounced vibrato. He did not glance at the door or the counter or any of the new customers passing by; he just continued to stare into the heart of some old reverie and hum — his face and neck jerking in sustained, rhythmic quivers.

I looked around once to see who else might be aware of the man. A nurse eating a hamburger stared at him a while before turning away in a kind of frustrated disbelief. A woman selecting post cards frowned as she slowly turned the rack around. But the regulars paid him no mind. The waitresses behind the counter joked and complained and called orders back and forth in a routine way. Even the cashier seemed oblivious of the strange humming man, or was at least making a definite effort to ignore him: she had turned sideways on her little hidden stool so that she faced into the cave of her notions and cigarettes, reading.

For a quarter of an hour I looked at the man, at the constant tremor of his face, and listened to his single fragment of a tune, hummed over and over, unvaryingly. And without knowing it was going to happen, I felt my flesh break into goose bumps and tears start draining toward my eyes — for suddenly the man at the candy counter seemed to be the most solitary person on earth. The drug store seemed to fade away, and I was standing on top of a high mountain watching as the man hummed what was left of his soul out into the universe. It was as though this pot-bellied man in the sleeveless shirt and tam o'shanter was creating his own private music for the spheres — music that had no sound, no echo, that simply joined his immense loneliness to the greater loneliness of space.

After a while the man stopped. His hand fell free of his wrist, he put the cigar into his mouth — and still without looking at anyone — he walked out of the drugstore into the street. The cashier knew he left, and that he did not pay, but she did not turn around.

Sunday Morning at Canutillo

✿ WHITE BUTTERFLIES above alfalfa; mountain ranges jutting into wide October blue. Cottonwoods along canals; a sense of space. . . .

That's Canutillo: easy blendings of earth and sky, where you can watch roads go peaceably between long green fields and scissortails rest on telephone poles and Mexican children play in the bare yards of adobe houses.

Over there a country church sits beside a cotton patch — with white dresses and yellow bolls mingling easily under the nine o'clock sun. Off a ways you can make out the adobe front of a crossroads store — and, wonderfully on it, the cool blue sign for Hamms beer.

Trucks, slatted, wait at a gin. Shadows gather beneath tall pecans. And as if it owned not only the land but life itself, cool October air keeps moving casually about — a feast for the senses. ❧

Ysleta

W OLD, PERSISTENT YSLETA: what has changed in three hundred years?

Well, the sun is still there. Each morning, low brown buildings turn their front walls toward it expectantly, like bland, weathered Mexican faces.

Sparrows — they still line the edges of roofs and play in trees and ride awkwardly on weeds. They are still as ever-present and unnoticeable as air and death, still scoot around in the dust as they did when quiet feet of the padres once moved about on the mission grounds.

Fat Mexican women, slow and elliptical in the distance, still make the daily trips into town from their farms, their children trailing behind like a loyal entourage of black-headed ducks.

(Other women — their arms folded, their stomachs pregnant, their faces locked in peaceable unconcern — stand talking in small backyards while their babies cry incessantly from dark windowless rooms.)

Old men in hats greasy at the base of the crown — they still hoe methodically in rectangles of broken earth, pausing only to glance upward at the sun and wipe their lined toothless faces with handkerchiefs almost as brown and old as themselves.

— Yes, stubborn Methuselah of the Texas past: what *has* changed in three hundred years? And what will change in three hundred more? Are you destined for a still longer and more graceful mortality — or is the day in view when you will sigh and give up the ghost and finally ascend to that most sanctified of all municipal Green Pastures: the one that blesses not with halos but with permanent historical markers?

II

On the Border:
Ciudad Juarez

Ten Sketches: A Day in Juarez

I : Morning, and Life

❧ IN JUAREZ, the world seems very much lived in. It is good just to walk down a street there in the mornings and see the dust, the bits of orange peel, the stray rocks scattered beside the curbs. Children sit cross-legged on the sidewalks, playing games, and women hurry along carrying sacks and pails. Life is a stuff, an essence, in the air, heady and strong — like the smell of fresh laundry borne on a good morning breeze.

Parrots have it as they shift about petulantly in their bamboo cages in the cool dark front windows. The boys on the sidewalk have it in their black watching eyes as they pull back a bare unwashed foot to let you pass by. Old street-cleaning men pushing slow brooms have it as they move down the curbs with their little dabs of trash, going toward the next shady chinaberry tree on the corner where they can stop and rest. Women have it in the very swelling tight firmness of their breasts. They step along with a strong carriage, and their legs, used to much walking, are as tightly rounded and firm in the calf as their breasts are. Watching them, you get the feeling that they are carrying life around invisibly on their heads, with the same deliberate ease that their Indian mothers once had when they carried baskets along the trails of the distant mountains.

Life, the forms of it, the tempo — how indelibly it is there each morning, as noticeable and unrelenting as the albino chow dogs who sit in the shade of doorways and level their amber eyes at familiar interests out in the bright sunlight ⋑

II : *The Room*

❧ WATCH MARIA CLEAN MY ROOM, watch her open all the east windows and let in the morning light. Watch her as she shakes my counterpane and smiles at the lint as it swims in the sunrays in a yellow aquatic ease.

For young María it is glorious to be in this big and airy room in the morning — in this room where the *americano* lives, where the green curtains suck in and out of the win-dows and make little brief pockets against the screens. She dusts with care, as if the room is a holy place, wiping the bottles and little boxes on the dresser tenderly and always setting them down again in their exact former places. She works surely and with dedication, progressing from the bed to the dresser to the desk with an accustomed rhythm, almost like that of an organist bending over familiar keys in an empty church.

As she works, things tempt her. She moves her dust rag over my typewriter and pauses to think how it would be to touch one of the white letters within the circles — touch it hard enough to make it jump inside the machine. My books tempt her. Each morning she takes them one by one from the shelf and wipes their covers, sometimes tracing the letters in the titles with her finger. Many times she has wanted to sit in the big chair by the window and open one of the books and look a long while at the words, but she is always afraid that she

would somehow, unknowingly, cause some kind of damage —
the way she was afraid that the typewriter was broken when
her rag got caught in the keys once and made the little bell
ring.

Sometimes, alone in the room, she wants to lean her head
and shoulders out one of the big windows and call down into
the courtyard and say, "Antonio, I'm up in the *americano's*
room — see?" She wants the old gardner to look up and shake
his head at her as if to say, Such a girl, such a girl. And she
wants to go right on smiling down at him and pull up her
shoulders in a great intake of fresh air. She wants to throw
out her hands and sing to the big pink mountains to the east.

When María daydreams she suddenly stops, a little a-
shamed, and hurries to finish her work. And after the room
is clean, she stands holding her hands about her broom and
gives one final glance around the bed and desk and books.
Then, upon leaving, she closes the door behind her as gently
as she can, as if it might be possible that I could hear her
and be pleased.   ⋟

III : *Willows*

❀ SOUTH OF TOWN the farmland stretches flatly out of sight,
and the single highway that passes across it provides the lure
of "other worlds." A man sitting beside the highway and
thinking loose thoughts on a warm day could be led to consider fanciful or strange things. He might stare at the hazy
line of the horizon or up into the heart of a willow tree and
get notions.

Such a man, a laborer, sits now beneath a group of tall
willows that arch down thickly around him at the edge of a

cotton field. He is eating tortillas and resting. His lunch is spread out between his legs on the old paper sack he has torn to make a plate. He takes a long time to chew his food, his temples flexing in a steady contented rhythm. He has put his straw hat on his knee and it rides there while he eats.

As he chews in the noon shade the man obligingly notices all things around him. He watches cars as they pass on the highway. He looks to the east where the thick, pinkish mountains are. Sometimes he is aware of the clouds, and studies them. But mainly he is concerned with the tall willows and their wild elegant limbs that have tumbled down about him in a green cascade. As he chews, his eyes keep scanning upward into their deep fountain of greenery. He finishes his lunch and leans back comfortably on his arm and dozes. Perhaps he dreams.

He is just an ordinary field hand, this man, and does not easily come down with a vagabond's fever from a little quiet noon relaxing. So there is no apparent change in him as he yawns after a while and picks up his straw hat and returns to his rows of cotton. Nevertheless, when the day ends and he leaves the field and returns to his little brown sunbaked hut on the edge of town, I'll bet you one thing: I'll bet he carried those willows with him. He'll speak to his wife and children in his usual unconcerned way and go about old after-work routines as always. But I'll bet those willows will be working on him. I'll bet in the hot, dry landscape of his mind there will be growing an intimate green scene — perhaps not one with words or even objects to it but instead just a gentle green lure, a willow-colored cast to his thoughts.

For it's just such innocent things that can affect the simplest man sometimes: a sense of space, some green trees, a little rumination.   ⟩

iv : *Club Tin Tan*

ⱳ IT IS A BAR ON 16 DE SEPTIEMBRE STREET. You enter the big airy room and there painted on the wall in his white zoot suit, white hat, and wide white smile is Tin Tan, the Mexican comic, his hand raised to you in greeting. If you are in a gloomy mood, you only have to look at the looping key chain, the thin elegant moustache — at Tin Tan's whole palm beach salutary air — to end up smiling a little inside. You can't help being lightened by this man who obviously doesn't take life quite as seriously as you do. So you relax and take your place at the bar and enjoy an after-dinner bottle of Carta Blanca.

It is pleasant there in the early afternoon. There is lots of natural soft light slanting down through the high windows facing the street, and the conversation of scattered twos and threes at the tables is always background mood music. No sound is ever hurried; even laughter rises and fades easily, without being forced. And whenever the juke box plays the loud, slow, melodramatic Mexican tunes, the men sitting at the bar in their hats pour their beer a little more slowly and carefully and look steadily ahead into the mirror behind the bar, as though studying themselves briefly and finding con-tentment in their images.

Sometimes a man, the owner perhaps, will open a small second-story window and look down into the bar from some hidden office. The little hole is just larger than his face — barely big enough to frame the smooth dark hair, the strongly hooked nose, the pale narrow face and its sleepy, heavy-lidded eyes. It is a shock each time to see the face: it is like looking up suddenly at the sad face of Manolete gazing down from heaven. The face usually lasts only a moment or two before the man draws back his head and closes the little door smoothly into the wall again.

If you stay long enough you watch the appearance of the big woman with oversized breasts. She comes out from a back room and stands with a great display of stateliness at the far end of the bar. She wears her hair upon her head and constantly touches the loose unruly strands that flow out at the back of her neck. She stands talking to the nearby men on the stools, occasionally accepting drinks, always blowing smoke from her cigarette toward her watching face in the mirror. Sometimes, when she shifts her weight about, her breasts sway in their great fluid whiteness almost like separate living things, making her seem no longer One but Three: a living Trinity of Flesh. ❧

v : *Dog in the Yard*

ꙮ TWO BOYS ARE STOPPED at a tall iron fence, looking at a
dog through the bars. He is lying on his back in the middle
of the yard, his legs sticking up stiff and straight in the air.

I ask, "Is he dead, you think?"

The boys shrug and stare on through the fence.

It is after two in the afternoon — late, you would think, for
a dead dog not to be found and hauled away.

"Hey, dogggg." The boys begin yelling at him. They whistle
and crow and shake the bars, but the dog does not stir.

He is a Boxer, and has a serious, capable-looking head. It
seems quite possible that he is simply relaxing in some eccen-
tric way: I can't recall having seen many Boxers asleep before.
But it is against reason. He is too still. He is like a metal lawn-
dog someone had shoved over during the night and has never
placed right-side up.

An old man passes us on the sidewalk while we watch and
I try to tell him that the dog seems dead. He nods and touches
his greasy felt hat amiably, saying, *"Buenos tardes, buenos
tardes,"* and then hobbles on by, obviously pleased by his
chance to talk. The boys shake at the bars in their last fierce
threats and then drift on up the street again, dragging their
sticks along the fence and laughing to each other in a big way.

The dog and I are finally alone, and I feel obligated to pass
judgment, somehow, on the scene — to make some assessment
or comment, to do anything in reaction. I look around again
to see if possibly I have missed some tell-tale sign or clue.
I look carefully at the dog, at his quiet yard, at all the barred
windows of his master's elegant grandee house. But there is
nothing significant.

I move on. After going a ways I look back, just in case. But
the Boxer has not moved. He still is lying upside down, rather
sober-looking and thoughtful, with his feet up. ꙮ

AS THE HEAT BEGINS TO GO OUT of the air and the walls of the adobe buildings allow their shadows to creep out across the sidewalks, you can see old women crossing the side streets of town in black headwraps and maroon shawls. They move tirelessly and fast, not limping down curbs the way you think old women should but hardly even stopping for them or noticing them. They are on errands, or coming home from work across the river, or out for a moment to scavenge in garbage cans. But they are all hurrying, all skimming along the dusty streets in their black moccasins like Chinese coolies pulling light invisible rickshaws, all with buckets in their hands or paper sacks, all finally disappearing suddenly around corners or into dark passageways.

The prostitutes do not hurry. They clatter along in their high heels and shiny black dresses, taking their time, not caring to get to the bars where they work any sooner than necessary. They do not solicit on the streets; they are working girls with a place of business and do not need to fool around on the sidewalks. At night, inside the bars, they sit perched on their stools like small bored gulls and call to the young American boys and lay their arms across their shoulders and ask for a drink. But now they are among their own people who know what it is to have to do such things for a living. The

Mexican men who pass them now will not be the ones who come to see them later in the bars; they will be selling hot dogs on a corner or trying to take pictures of tourists in the clubs or helping to park cars. It is only the Americans who mill in and out of the swinging bar doors at night, who go upstairs. It is only the Americans who have money.

Americans, sex, money — these are the prostitutes' three fates pulling the young women slowly and inevitably down the old narrow streets in their wobbling heels and loud-smelling Woolworth perfume. ❧

VII : *Five O'clock Salesmen*

W HE STANDS IN THE DOORWAY of his shop near the international bridge, calling idly across the street to other salesmen in other shops while he waits for tourists. He yawns and laces his fingers together and stretches lazily and folds himself forward and pops his knuckles down by his knees, exploding in wild bent-over laughter as his friends across the way shout an ending to a joke. He straightens up slowly and just in time to see a tourist strolling toward him. Instantly, but without a show of hurrying, he assumes his vendor's pose. He puts his hands behind his back, decorously, and rocks forward slightly from his doorway almost directly into the tourist's path, quickly reciting his offer of leather goods and jewelry and figurines. But since it is only five o'clock, there is no real attack. It is much too early for the main crowd. There is no use spreading all the nets for a few isolated fish. So he allows the tourist to shake his head and pass on by. He raises his shoulders and sways his body after him from his stationary feet, exaggerating the tourist's offhanded shrug.

Since it is not quite dark yet, the salesman is just trifling with time. He yawns again, hugely and vacantly, recovering long enough to comment loudly across the street to the other salesmen standing in their own doorways. He gazes down the street, up the street, finally notices a black dog that has been wandering along in the gutter and has ended up looking blankly into his door. He strikes up a conversation with the dog, asking him if he would not like a new wallet or perhaps a set of earrings for his lady friend. The dog looks steadily at the salesman, who now moves out of the doorway, bowing and inviting the dog to step inside. The salesman becomes bored and flips a match; it hits the dog near his ear. The dog jerks his leg down and looks around cautiously and eases on down the street, still looking into the shops.

The salesman takes a brief survey of his pants and brushes at flecks of dust. He tries calling something across the street again, but no one hears him. He decides to check the time. He pushes his coat sleeve away from his watch: it is only five after five.

🔥 ALONG THE RAILROAD TRACKS quiet men in worn clothes are going home from work. They are not walking together, not in twos or groups for companionship; each walks a little apart from the others, isolated. As they move along no one talks much, no one expends any effort in passing the time of day. And there is no need for that, really, for as they walk they communicate enough. Their steadily moving legs, their old mismatched and worn clothes, their solemn and deep-lined brown faces — these speak everything that needs to be said. As they walk along they share, without words, the essentials — the poverty, the daily hardships of their lives. So what could there be new in a day to talk about? Occasionally, of course, friends do happen to pass, but even in greeting the men seldom slow in their walking: there is a called word or two, a raised hand or shrugged shoulder, a louder or repeated word, a fading reply, and the exchange is done.

The many steady figures keep on, appearing after a while not to be just a bunch of ordinary men trudging home from work but, instead, something grander and more subtly awesome — perhaps the first insignificant, trickling wave of a great force of men who have finally taken all they could of poverty and hardship and have put aside their few farm tools and old vendor's carts and stone mason's trowels for the final time and are walking out of Mexico into the United States, coming the way a great swarm of locusts might, moving across the new rich lands in a great silent advancing drove. . . .

The tracks make a long open clearing through the middle of town. It is very quiet here when the trains are out, almost like a seashore, somehow, with a great wideness between the buildings on either side and an open length down the track meeting the peaceful stretches of sky.

It has rained during the week and there are still big pubbles standing along the tracks. The men detour past them, being careful even in their old shoes and frayed pants to avoid muddy places.

You see on the east side a few old men who have stopped to sit on the concrete porch of one of the long warehouses and take the last rays of the sun. It is directly in their faces now and on the white walls of the warehouse. The concrete porch is very warm for them and the men will sit comfortably and silently until night falls.

Across on the west side the buildings cast heavy shade on the damp, muddy ground. Occasionally a big truck with loose sideboards comes slushing along the narrow street that runs between the west buildings and the tracks, the driver not slowing down at all for the puddles or the mud, going along as fast as he would ordinarily on a good street, bouncing high out of the deep mudholes and rattling the sideboards and weaving some in the ruts. The man driving the truck is without a hat and has a growth of beard and hair. He sits hunched forward a little in the cab and it doesn't seem to matter to him particularly if the truck makes it to its destination or drives straight on into hell or falls apart there on the street and disappears down into the mud. It would all be the same — for what is there in Mexico for him anyway except having children and being poor and trying to forget them both? He goes sloshing and bouncing on down the little street and turns a corner fast, spraying a stiff-walking old man with mud as he turns. The old man, carrying a strapped bundle of firewood on his back, doesn't even look up.

At the back porch of one of the wooden warehouses a vendor sells bottled orange drinks to the passersby. He doesn't have a regular vendor's stand — just the bottles set on the porch steps and an empty case. By age he is a young man —

say about 21 — but with his old faded blue suit coat and khaki pants, his ragged haircut, and his slow, disinterested manner, he is no younger really than the old man just splashed with mud. Poverty makes most men in Juárez look the same.

Every now and then, one of the men going home along the tracks will stop to buy an orange drink. He lights up a cigarette, too, throwing back his head to exhale as he talks to the vendor. The smoke bursts into sight above his head like a blossom, a very sudden and delicate bluish-white blossom. It grows and gradually dies there against the sky made clear and pure from the rains.

Watching, you wish that the young vendor might notice the smoke and its lazy, curling elegance; but it fades and he does not see it. Neither does the man stopping for the drink — nor would any of the men walking home along the tracks. Only an outlander, a visitor — one who does not live in Juárez — only he would be sufficiently free to notice such a thing as smoke, or the great spaciousness of the tracks. Only he would bother with beauty. A vendor can only pick up empty bottles and put them in a case and then stand beside his porch, pulling splinters from a board and chewing them. ❧

IX : *The Young Men*

IN THE EARLY EVENING feminine young men parade by twos and threes along the sidewalks of the downtown plaza, stopping now and then at tree-shadowed benches to sit and talk. As they talk their hands, their arms, the upper halves of their bodies — all are in constant motion, the way marine plants move and feel idly about on an ocean's floor. Sometimes, on dark nights, their lightly waving hands and heads fuse with the swaying movements of the tree limbs in the background and become one little rhythmic force. And their melodic, airy sounds, rising and falling away gradually into the night — they seem not like words spoken by secret, hidden mouths, but more like fluttering leaves, dropped onto the air by the continually waving, seaweed hands.

On some private signal the young men rise quickly together, as though suddenly remembering some distant appointment — one of them leading, the other one or two hurrying along just slightly behind. Together they float out from under the trees: their small feet pointed inward a little, V-shaped, as they take their quick, precisioned steps, and their elbows and hands and heads all moving in separate directions, each part alive and slightly wobbling, like those of puppets. They move as if controlled by delicate weights and balances within their bodies, and would crumple into lifeless rag dummies there on the sidewalk if you suddenly stepped up to them and cut some inner vital cord.

As they move out of sight in their hurrying yet strangely static way, they are like characters who stepped out of a Dagwood Bumstead cartoon strip just long enough to take a stroll across the plaza. If you squint hard after them as they round a corner, you can even see just barely trailing behind them that wavy, broken line the artist always uses to indicate motion.

x : *Darkness, and the Canal*

℟ AFTER NIGHT HAS SETTLED you move away from the neon streets near the international bridge and you go to the parts of town where there are no tourists. You go to where Juárez lies waiting as a true Mexican town, as a place of darkness.

There, among shadowed walkers and silhouetted trees, you learn that no one tries to conquer the night as they try to do so often in other places. Night exists in its own blackness; it is not contested by great commercial areas of pseudo-day. Night is accepted on its own terms and is responded to with welcome. People move within it comfortably, easily, as fish move through deep silent seas. And if lights are used, they are used as means of temporary relief from an acknowledged greater power. They are used as shade is during the day — to assuage, a bit, the main reality.

To be sure, small dim bulbs are lit on scattered street corners, and children gather near them to snatch a few last scenes out of the day. They run in and out of the pale yellow circle on the dusty street, shouting excited cries, dragging behind them everywhere their long quivering shadows. But even the children don't believe that the bulbs are doing battle with the night. They know that they are just staunch little islands of light, serving only to accentuate the vast waters of the dark.

After walking a while — after entering deeply into this town of walls and darkened streets and medieval air — you come to sit beside the dry, crumbling canal that winds through the west part of town. There, resting, you hear others like yourself passing by in the muffling dust. You hear lone dogs barking in the distance, somehow sounding right on the very edge of the night. You hear low voices of lovers from a building's shadow, and voices of people walking home down in the dry bed of the canal — hollow voices, yet strangely heightened, as though coming from a cave or filtering up through the crust of the earth. Sometimes there is the sound of old cars gunning in second gear for long distances on nearby streets, going across the night with wildness, then returning along a parallel street a few moments later, again in second gear, still gunning — sounding like mechanical racing dogs who have gone mad or been fed ground glass, running violently everywhere and nowhere, trying desperately to find relief.

And then, when it is very late and all the old men's feet seem to have passed in the dust for the last time and all the doors across town are finally quieting, you look across the canal to where a young girl sits reading in a vendor's stand. She is hunched over in the stall, reading a magazine by candlelight, and is barely visible above the counter top. A row of red and orange soft drinks stands on the counter before her, and magazines hang diagonally about the stand.

You wonder how long the girl has been there, so still, and how long she will remain. It is past midnight. You look at her hair, shining a rich glossy Indian black in the candlelight. You look about once more at the night, so encompassing, so total, except for that small glow of light within the stand. Finally you fall to watching the candle on the counter top: despite the breezes that fitfully scatter the dust along the banks of the canal, not once does the flame of the candle waver. It bores up through the darkness in the full rigid form of a classic flame. It sits there, pointed and clean, as though subject to no temptation.

And it almost makes a believer of you, here in Catholic Mexico—almost makes you ready to believe it possible that an angel of purity could descend and invest herself in a candle flame just so a little vendor girl might have the steadying hint of God to comfort her on dark and lonesome nights.

Conquistador

❧ HE IS JUST A SHOE SHINE MAN, but he moves along Mariscal Street in Juárez with the air of a Spanish explorer. He is monumentally dirtied and almost as monumentally haired. His beard, black and wiry, coils and juts about his face with a debonair boldness.

He wears a tasseled hat — not an ordinary straw, but a kind of Aussie campaign hat, with the gold tassel looped around the crown and hanging in double strands down the back.

He doesn't have on a shirt; he wears a short maroon jacket with an Eisenhower cut, very dirty, yet fitting trimly and militarily around his waist. His pants, once white, are full and pegged at the bottom and much too short — there are wide stretches of dirty ankle above his shoes. The pants are held up by a cotton rope, tied in a knot to one side.

He makes his rounds from bar to bar, the shoe shine box strapped diagonally across his back with two jointed leather belts — like a carbine. He enters each pair of swinging doors, makes his questing little tour inside, then emerges again a few moments later — wholly unperturbed at not finding a customer, still swinging jauntily along the sidewalk like an alpinist making his way toward the Matterhorn.

If you got just a glimpse of him from a distance you might think he was one of Captain Kidd's men striding down the back street of some Caribbean village. He maintains that easy, swashbuckling gait. And you feel, too, that whenever he does find someone willing to have his shoes shined, he will give the customer a single confident nod, swing his wooden box off his shoulder, and begin making preparatory swipes with his brush the same way a fencer loosens up with initial thrusts of his foil — with the same gracefully-bold assurance.

Obviously this is a man of parts, of prominence, a man cast in the mold of Cyrano de Bergerac and Lafitte and D'Artagnan. It was simply his fate to be born in the wrong era and the wrong circumstances — so that instead of approaching life with rapier and arquebus he must content himself with the weapons of Mariscal Street — polishing rags and a can of Shinola.

West Juarez

STRETCHING AWAY from the hidden banks of the Rio Grande toward the dusty mountains in the south, West Juárez seems part of another hemisphere. It is like some lonely desert city of Asia Minor, a primitive hill town of Berbers or Arabs.

From a distance — from across the river in El Paso — nothing seems to move. Of course, now and then a boy can be seen running along a dune; a brief section of laundry will flap on a line; occasionally there is the figure of a man, a sign of smoke, a dog. But they are not really noticeable; they do not consti-

tute the scene. What is there is the array of adobe cubes sitting implacably in the sun — the solid rectangles and squares scattered aimlessly across the sand like hundreds of small brown boxes.

A place of squatters, it has no visible trees, no yards, no streets — just trails here and there, eroded ridges and bluffs, arroyos. Silence, rather than a community of people, seems to live there — it, and poverty and space: elements and the elemental.   ❧

At the Dog Track

🐾 MY ATTENTION WAS CAUGHT by a short, swarthy man who was looking fixedly at his racing form. He was very serious — scowling continuously at the paper through the heavy fog of his cigarette—and had thick, delicately-shaped lips. He wore a dark sports coat, white shirt without a tie, black elevator shoes.

Watching him, I found that he affected my imagination strongly. I tried to visualize him as he must have looked, say, as a one-year-old standing in his crib: he was already hairy and was already wearing elevator shoes for babies. Casually holding a rubber nipple between his fingers like a cigarette, he frowningly calculated the odds on something — perhaps giving 8 to 1 against a cruising fly landing upon a nearby dirty diaper. . . .

My reverie, however, was short-lived: the lights dimmed in the *galgodromo,* the greyhounds broke from their gates, and the crowd began shouting to its favorites. The scowling man alone didn't move, took no part in the excitement; he just continued to stare down into his racing form. There was a roar at the finish and the lights went up and as the results were announced over the loudspeaker a small group of winners hurried across to the betting windows. The scowling man ignored them, looked at his form a moment longer, then flicked his hand against it in disgust and lowered it to his side. He squinted deeply into space, his mouth dropped slightly ajar, his cigarette tilting to his chin. For a moment I thought he was on the verge of speech — of letting loose a violent Mafia oath of revenge, or making an appeal for dog-racing justice to some impartial celestial observer, or perhaps simply cursing, bitterly, at the overwhelming stupidity of a track that would allow Lucky Jim to fade in the eighth. But he ended up saying nothing. He merely brought up the racing form, joggled it about in the air as though trying to shake the nonsense off it or get it into better focus, then began to regard it again with deep hostility through his steaming cigarette.

III

Hill Country

A Visit Home

ꟷ HARRY'S FOLKS still lived in the hill country of Central Texas, and in the summertime Harry liked to go back there and stay a while. He liked it when the camps along the river were open and tourists were around town and things were generally relaxed and green and summery. He liked just being around his home, too, getting some August sun and doing a little work in the yards. It seemed to clean him out good and help get his mind straight to be able to use his hands again, to swing a hammer against a broken gate or pull weeds or paint a strip of weathered boards. And Harry's folks, of course, were always glad when he was back. He was easy to have around the house and the three of them got along well together. They didn't get on each other's nerves.

Some of the mornings after breakfast Harry got into his old clothes and gathered up rags and a turpentine jar and cans of paint and he painted on the house or maybe a section of fence. He liked painting: he liked the easy, mindless stroking of brush against wood, the slow erasing of old surfaces and the friendly spread of new ones. And he liked it best of all when he worked on the front fence next to the street. It was always pleasant there on his knees in the cool bermuda grass, making the old palings grow clean and white. The oaks and young hackberries along the fence waved light summer shadows about him, and the paint and turpentine smelled pungent and clean. Locusts would be in the trees along the street, and doors throughout the neighborhood slammed casually back and forth during the long mornings. Sometimes Harry could hear an ice-cream wagon moving slowly and peacefully by, ringing its bell.

After working all morning Harry would scrub up a little with kerosene and change clothes and walk down to a small neighborhood grocery store to buy a bottle of beer. It was a familiar walk, past many of the same old houses he knew as a child — the same deep yards, the same high, dust-covered trees, the same noontime angles of shade covering the porches and cement walks. He enjoyed walking straight down the middle of the dusty, unpaved streets, bareheaded and in the sun, watching the dogs run to bark at him through their picket fences — the same way dogs of his childhood did.

Usually during summertime one street or another in the neighborhood would be under repair — paving or grading or maybe oiling — and the smell of hot tar or oil or even just the huge shiny metal bulk of road machinery would make the noonday of such a street abnormally hot. But Harry didn't mind; he even liked it. Being hot, thoroughly and brutally hot — that was as good during summertime as being cool. He would smile in a kind of private stoic joy at the heat burning into his face and arms and the sweat prickling in his skin. To Harry there was something beautiful and exciting about the heat of a summer noontime — about the locusts singing long and wildly in sidewalk trees and the sun almost seeming to eat down through the sky with its terrific glare and the white frame houses sitting very tidy and modest and subdued behind their yards, as though intimidated a little by the rough vigor of such a masculine noon.

After Harry bought the beer and a package of Fritos and walked back home, he sat on his front porch and rested a little before dinner. He tilted his beer bottle slowly — the dark brown kind with the tall neck — and he looked out to the oaks and the grass of the yard. Down the street a neighbor had the radio on, getting the noon weather report and live-stock market news. That was a comfortable program for Harry to listen to. He knew that all across the hill country, ranch families were sitting around their dinner table now, tuned in to hear how many points of rain fell overnight in San Angelo or Luling and where the low-pressure systems were over the state and what the chances were for rain in the next couple of days. Harry didn't care himself about low-pressure systems or rain in Luling, but somehow it pleased him to think about how much the ranch people cared for such things, how they would be including the weatherman's comments in their party-line conversations that afternoon: ". . . yes, well, old Henry Howe said at noon there might be a chance for a few late-afternoon thundershowers, but I'm not going to hold my breath none." Harry would sit there on the porch, not really listening to the actual words of the weatherman but rather to the sound of them; and when Henry Howe began his long wrap-up of feed and cattle quotations, using all the special, singsong phrases — "sheep: 600; active, mostly steady; ewes strong to 50 cents higher . . . good and choice stocker calves $22.50 to $28.00" — such words and figures went beyond language and to Harry became a kind of lulling, dreamlike chant of noon folk music, a kind of casual and inviting vocal guitar.

In the evenings after supper, when his mother would be out watering in the dusky shadows of the yard and his father would be out back working in the garden, Harry would get into his car and drive off slowly toward town. Summer nights were always the same there in his home town, but to Harry that was their lure and even their peace. He drove out by the Dairy Queen on the north highway to see the people waiting patiently on the smooth gravel in front of the small window screen — just as they had waited the previous night and the many nights before that. He would drive to the other edge of town and then slowly back along the main street to see what was on at the show, passing the other lone, slowly-cruising cars and the other lone drivers. Sometimes he would park and buy a Dallas or San Antonio paper at the newsstand and with it folded underneath his arm he would walk along past the dark storefronts, seeing how they all felt and looked at night with their doors locked and their merchandise silent and inaccessible behind glass. At the side of the Robert E. Lee, the main hotel in town, a bellboy in his faded blue uniform would be standing at the curb, taking an eight-o'clock smoke and idly keeping tab on the cars that kept wandering by.

Occasionally Harry drove up the river road past the summer camps, the small hillside farms, the spacious summer homes of the well-to-do that would be lit by strings of yellow lights stretched among many somber yard trees. Nighttime along the river was always nice in the summer, and Harry sometimes stopped for a while at a low-water crossing and turned off his lights. He would sit listening to the pleasant river sounds — the many frogs, the katydids and crickets — and he would smell the refreshing cleanness of the river air. Lightning bugs were usually off in the distance, directly over the water or perhaps deep among the tall cypress trees, almost hidden. Sometimes a small waterfall would be downriver just within hearing. Harry would sit in his car, tired from his day's work, listening to the strong, lulling rhythm of the frogs and the heavy sounds of the big tourist cars that passed over the bridge and then lunged away up the opposite slope toward town. Usually he grew sleepy, his mind and body sagging into the peaceful dark of the river and the night, and he would have to wrench himself into the notion of going back home. For the first few miles he opened his small window wing and let the cool summer air off the hay fields and the river flow hard into his face, bathing it back to taut alertness.

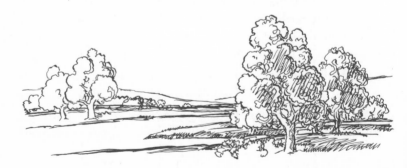

Harry's folks owned a piece of ranchland north of town, a wooded, rocky place passed on to his family from Harry's grandfather. There was no house on it, just an old hunter's cabin that Harry and his father kept working on little by little during summertime. Several times a week Harry took his lunch and worked out there all day. In addition to the cabin improvements, fences were always in need of repair and the livestock needed to be seen after.

It was a nice thirty-minute drive out from town. For about ten miles the highway kept close to the north fork of the river, with a heavy green line of sycamores always in sight beyond the small bordering fields of grain and hay. Then a farm-to-market road turned off the highway and after winding first through a close little walnut valley it gradually rose upward to the higher plateau of ranch country. Some of the land there was free of timber, and the sheep and goats and cattle grazed in open stretches of grass within sight of the road. Most of the land, however, was wooded with live oaks and cedars and the small shin oak trees that goats like to eat on. Country lanes turned off the road every so often, gently bending a-round a line of fence and going to the neat ranch homes set off in the distance in a slump of trees. Sometimes one of them could be seen from the road — perhaps a cool-looking flag-stone house with a curving archway in front of its porch and a border of tall red-topped cannas along either side.

Near the top of the plateau Harry would leave the farm-to-market road and drive about a mile through his folks' place down to the cabin — a rock-and-tin building set in the low center of several sloping hills, with pens and water tanks and small clearings all around. There was a little dry hollow that ran south from the pens under a trail of Spanish oak and wal-nut trees, and along it were rocky shelves and ledges where a stream once made its way into the lower flat land of the pastures.

It was never lonely for Harry as he worked out there in the country. To him everything was friendly — the sun on the grass, the flint and caliche rocks scattered about under the trees, the coiled strand of smooth tie-wire hanging here and there around the tops of fence posts. Sheep were always bleating and calling from the ridges; heavy-bellied red Hereford cows wandered in from the pastures to get water and lie up under the shade. Black squirrels dashed from secret tunnels beneath the cabin to their homes down beyond the corral. Sometimes bumblebees got down in the thick, sweet-smelling sage along the fences and moved across the blossoms like clumsy old burghers with knotty canes. And ever so often, in a sudden intense blaze of color and noise, there appeared pairs of small reddish birds that suspended themselves in the sky: with their tail feathers fluffed and spread out like miniature turkey gobblers' and their small red wings waving frantically for support, for minutes on end they would hang there and sing little shrill, wild, quarrelsome melodies directly into each other's face.

After dinner, when the sun was directly overhead and the day had settled into its long afternoon exercise in heat, Harry might stretch out for a while along the shaded ravine on top of a cool rocky shelf. As he lay there under the Spanish oaks he would sometimes hear from a hillside the single, idle tinkling of a sheep's bell. And with the day so explosively dry and hot it was almost as though the hot air itself out in the pastures had made a small crystalline sound, a single comment about itself to the afternoon. Somehow this would make Harry restless, would stir up in him the desire to be out deeper within the pastures and the heat; so he would gather up an armload of small cedar staves from out at the corral and he would go along one of the fencelines that led away from the cabin, wiring a stave against the fence here and there where it sagged. It was a simple chore, just taking pliers and short pieces of smooth tie-wire and securing the small slim cedar poles against the fence so it would have a little added strength. But out there in the pasture in the long afternoon, among the trees and grass and steady heat, wiring staves was somehow to Harry a handsome thing to do. It was good to be in a place where you could fix something like a fence and wipe away sweat now and then with the back of a sleeve and afterward stand looking out across the ground to your rocks and your trees, knowing that you were where you should be, knowing you were home.

Occasionally Harry's father would take an afternoon off from his feed store in town and would come out with Harry to work at the cabin. He was not a big man but he was used to working long, hard hours. The two of them always worked steadily and well together.

It never failed that when they were out there at the cabin — working, say, at repairing the roof — Harry's father would look up from driving a nail to squint at the sun and say, "What about it, son, you ready for some of that good stud-horse coffee?" Harry would nod, saying he guessed it was about that time, and together they would lay aside their hammers and climb down from the roof and go around to the east side of the cabin where there was a little shade. Usually it would be just about the right time for coffee — between four and five, when the main burden of the afternoon heat had begun to lift and the sun was already deeply committed toward the line of oak trees rimming the west. Harry's father liked strong coffee — studhorse strong, as he called it — and he especially liked it during the summertime when he and Harry worked together out at the cabin.

He would begin chopping sticks for kindling and building a small fire while Harry took the big smoke-blackened coffee pot around to the windmill and washed it out. Then, after the fire was made and the coffee pot was steadied on top of the crossed burning sticks, and a pair of washed tin cups were set in the open cabin window, the two of them sat on an old bench in the shade of the cabin to watch the fire grow hotter and to look out at the gradually settling afternoon. Both Harry and his father had their straw hats off, and both their khaki shirts were darkened from heavy sweating. Both sagged forward a little on their knees.

As they sat there Harry knew his father was content, knew that it was a pleasure for him to be there sitting on the bench beside his son while the two of them waited for the coffee to boil. Harry could feel the pleasure. His father didn't show it openly; he just sat chewing his small wad of tobacco and squinting off into the pastures beyond the corral. They didn't talk much; they waited on the coffee and rested. But Harry knew that his father usually didn't chew tobacco except when he was off somewhere by himself — maybe late in the afternoon when he worked in the garden or early in the mornings while doing up the chores in back of the house. Chewing there on the bench with Harry was a sign of his ease and comradeship. Even just gazing into the pastures — Harry knew that was something, too. His father was not a person to spend his time gazing; he was one to be fixing a loose board in a porch floor or rehanging a gate so it would swing better. To actually sit down and lean over on his hunkers a little and cast even the most casually interested eye outward: to actually get close to ruminating on the scene before him — that was something very rare and revealing.

Harry knew he had not shared much time with his father after growing up — he remembered how often they had gone fishing together when Harry was a boy, how the two of them would sit on the riverbank during long Sunday afternoons. They had done a lot of that kind of sharing and being together — not really talking about anything, just the two of them joined by the act of fishing and made content by it. But after high school, after Harry left home and began living in other towns and just visited back with his folks now and then, there hadn't seemed to be anything to join them together again except words. They would talk in the front room at home on holidays or while driving someplace to visit relatives with Harry's mother. But it would just be fact-talk, an exchange of news and family happenings. It was only when words weren't needed — like at the cabin, working outdoors and waiting for coffee, or like the Sundays years before along the river — that the two of them could bridge the awkward gap of words and come to a kind of union again.

As Harry thought about it he knew that it was worth coming home just to give his father a moment of old companionship, for them to be able to sit down together, both sweating, both in the same kind of old worn clothes, both tired and waiting for the hard clean smell of coffee to rouse their spirits a little. It was worth having his father sit there beside him without awkwardness or strain: for his father to enjoy the knowledge that Harry was indeed still his son, had not gradually and subtly evaporated beyond reach but was still someone to be close to, someone he could still look at and call his own.

And once, as his father rose from the bench to see how the coffee was coming along, Harry looked at him and thought, with sudden amazement: why, my God, I'm still this man's flesh and blood and he has never forgotten it, not for a moment, even though I haven't given him anything of myself except news for the last fifteen years. Harry watched his father carefully take the pot off the fire with his handkerchief and begin to pour into the cups on the window sill. He thought: how easy it is never to know how a father would feel about a son; how easy to overlook that a man would go right on feeling he was someone's father long after the son had gone away, had gathered up his life like a neat bundle of clothes so that nothing was left of it around home any more except the empty hangers in a closet — old reminders and memories.

And so the two of them would sit with cups in their hands, sometimes drinking briefly, mostly waiting for the coffee to cool: an aging man with false teeth and a chew of tobacco in his jaw; a younger man, his son, just home for a while, visiting.

Two O'clock, and Red Flowers

EVERY DAY a hill country ranchman is up before six, moving about in the coolness, milking and scattering hay in the back pens and looking out across the maize and oat fields lying quiet in the bare early light. Sometimes after breakfast he takes a quick run into town in his pickup to get some washers for a windmill or a couple of jars of sheep drench; but he's usually back before nine. And then, well, there is riding to be done along the fences in the pastures, and wormy sheep to be tended to, and maybe even the rods in the windmill to be pulled. With his wife it is the same thing: going steady from before sunup, getting breakfast and straining the milk and cleaning up the house and dampening the clothes and gathering and silking the corn from the garden and in general getting things moving along in the right way toward dinner time.

But when it finally gets to be two o'clock — that's when it is a ranchman's nap-time. To him there is nothing more sensible and necessary after dinner than to have his shoes off and be stretched out sound asleep in the back bedroom next to an open window — his white-cotton-socked feet resting one on top of the other, neatly, his mouth open and slightly pooching and pouting with each long, relaxing escape of breath.

If you would happen to drive up to this ranchman's house right at two, you would be struck by the quietness of it, the complete sense of rest nurtured by an almost friendly heat. The house would be set off from the road on a slight rise of ground and surrounded by oak and pecan trees that would be very green and calm and somehow almost domesticated. You would notice a windmill behind the house — just the top of it, the fan, visible above the roof — and then, looking about, you would see the scattering of pens and barns and water troughs and a cement tank or two.

You would notice that the house itself is neat, in good repair, with new white paint on the window frames and underneath the eaves. The front-yard fence would be the kind most ranchmen have in the hill country: the tight, strong-looking, smooth-wire kind, with the top wire going along in little regular, arcing waves. The yard would be in two sections on either side of the flagstone walk; perhaps it would be recently mowed, with faint, gently curving patches of confetti-like grass still trailing here and there. On the porch — which would by now be caught in a mild afternoon shadow — the chairs and the rocker would seem inviting and open and still full of greeting, as if the ranchman and his wife had at that very moment risen out of them and stepped indoors.

These are the things your glance would take in at first — the

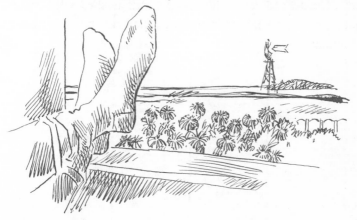

obvious, simple pleasures of the resting house and its surroundings. Yet there would be something else there, too —
something perhaps not too noticeable as you drive up, something seemingly quite innocent and even uninvolved in the
scene.

It would be the row of red, long-stemmed flowers that the
ranch people call old maids, standing in their clean, well-
tended bed next to the small porch. Standing there, just at
that time of day, with so much silence and heat and rest in
the air, they would gradually seem more than just themselves,
more than just flowers: they would seem like a round-faced,
heat-flushed, well-behaved children's chorus. They would
seem almost to be smiling, as though they neither sweated
nor wilted nor were in the least way affected by the great
heat. Dry-stemmed, hardy, very much at ease, they would
look out contentedly on two o'clock — as if a ranch afternoon
were one long, held breath and they could hold their breath
longer than anyone. And if you would happen to look their
way, they would seem to be nodding and wobbling a greeting
to you just slightly, as if saying with an immensely subdued
but genuine courtesy: "Well, *hello* . . . the rest of the folks
are asleep right now but won't you come in, anyway? We're
sure they'll be glad to see you." And with another nod they
would withdraw from the conversation and stand in their
red, poised hardiness — like sensible domestics who had attended to the social amenities and then retired into respectful silence. ϶

Hill Country Camp Meeting

❦ THE BIG THING on the congregation's mind is the preacher — will he look good, does he sing, is he impressive? To be in the tradition of the best ones of the past, he should have traveled from a respectably far-off place like Houston or Dallas or Brownsville. He should wear white shoes, still be somewhat young but with a quietly-firm jaw. It helps if he is brunette and has an executive tan. Of course he must have a beautiful young wife and small child, and they must sit on the front bench near the pulpit where he can nod and smile in their direction during the opening remarks of his sermon (remarks designed to show how warmly human he is; to demonstrate, charmingly, his own personal fallibility). Both the wife and child must wear nice starched clothes and both must appear as an obviously rich reward and blessing for a favored man of God.

Yet he cannot have these qualifications and fail to be high-powered; he cannot lead the people into the big open-air tabernacle with his calmly commanding air and soulfully sunken eyes and then stand on the speaker's platform and be somebody they all could have heard in town. Above all else he must bring the message of power they have filed in to hear. He must stand there with a fist leveled in their faces and shame them; he must catalogue their many sins and have them look nakedly into the deep moral abyss of their souls; he must shake them with his words as a dog would shake rabbits until they sit in purged passivity. He must thunder down at them and then be dynamically silent; he must thunder and be silent once again. Then he must become a prowling lion of Jesus, slashing at sin with his righteous claws. And at the proper moment, just before the roars lose their power and their weight and their credibility, he must suddenly be a lion no more; he must gradually regain the quietly elegant form

of God's humble and moral man. He must taper to the hush
of the Garden, and then be still.

All of this he must do in exactly thirty minutes — from 11:30
until 12:00 — for evangelical gusto is a two-edged sword that
must be skillfully handled, especially at camp meetings. He
must always remember, even in the supreme moments of his
oratorical splendor, that twelve noon is the witching hour for
men who would come before their fellows to tell them what
to do for everlasting grace. He must remember that the three
main reasons for a summer camp meeting — preaching and
eating and visiting — are championed with equal stoutness;
and should he happen to succumb to the glory of his own
voice and edge the gospel over into lunchtime, such an act
of intemperance will go hard on him and the pure image of
him in the people's mind will be badly smudged. He must
realize that to the rows of captive men who have sat out their
dutiful hour, after-twelve preaching is always a breach of
camp-meeting code and that although they agreeably suspend their personalities for a while in the expectation of win-
ning the community's salvation, at twelve o'clock they automatically switch their reasons back on. He must be shrewd
enough to know that it is not possible for any preacher — regardless of his pretty smiling wife and his white shoes and his

years along the Amazon — to retain full status among such a group of men if he takes lightly their hour's sacrifice and thereby implies that grace, in the long run, is more important than barbeque.

These men, these husbands in stiff Sunday clothes, sitting erect on the hard, splintery benches, holding babies straight in their laps with both hands around them as if they were dolls or flower vases — they demonstrate in this camp meeting hour a strange stoic quality which they do not show anywhere else. They manage an almost saintly composure. While their women folk begin to fan briskly in the August heat and comment tersely behind their fans about covered dishes getting cold out in the car and how they never did get to go to the bathroom at home because they had been in such a rush, these men sit as though they had totally suspended reason and judgment and attention, as though they had silently attached their minds to small balloons and let them rise to the roof of the tabernacle. And content to be free of them for the duration of the sermon, the men simply sit and look polite. When the whole business is finally over and the crowd begins to rise and loosen itself for dinner, the men know that they will have plenty of time then to summon their thoughts down from the roof and begin formulating congratulatory words for the preacher.

Always at such gatherings there are old women with moles on their chins and white-turning-to-yellow hair full of old-fashioned combs. There are small hair-lipped boys who stay close to their mothers' skirts in the barbeque line and stare out at the crowd with fearful eyes. Sometimes there is an old toothless man who after the service makes his headquarters beside the water tank where the other men come to stand in the shade and drink from the dipper and talk. He generally finds himself shaking hands every now and then with men from town who are quite surprised to see him there — they were under the impression he had died some years before. ("Well," one of the men will ask him, "who *was* it I thought died, then?") And nearly always there will be at least one small boy listening behind a blue hymnal to old women too crippled to leave the tabernacle at dinner — old women talking of "tumors" and "an aching uterus" and using other compelling and magical terms that the little boy vows to use on his friends when he gets back home. ➤

Summer Evening

🔥 DAY IS LONG IN QUITTING, the summer twilight long and mild like a deep soft hole in time itself that has opened now just before dark.

The air seems to have thickened and blurred, and trees balloon darkly behind themselves into spreading shades. Chickens going to roost within the trees look like scraps of white paper pasted against the leaves. In the garden where you work, the ground grows thick and solid — an immensely sober and familiar thing resisting the time of mysterious change.

And all of a sudden, when you aren't expecting it, night falls. You are looking past the wire fence of the garden into a patch of hoarhound and weeds below — just for a moment letting your mind blend with the twilight, letting it reach out and touch the vagueness of the air — when suddenly two katydids begin to sing and you look back to the fence and it is gone, dissolved. Night has descended on the earth, bringing with it its own sounds: cars hum and rattle and speed on neighboring streets, doors of houses slam more noticeably, katydids increase their singing.

You walk across the soft, loose, yielding dirt of the garden to the gate, putting your arm through and by instinct finding the latch. As the gate swings open a cow lows with a long distant eloquence somewhere to the south. You stand a moment, listening, your face pointed in the darkness toward the lowing as if your eyes could still see. You stand there, suspended somewhere between listening and thinking, until you finally shut the gate and walk up the slope of the rocky yard toward your house, where the yellow light of the kitchen window shines like a beacon through the trees.　　　　⌁

Late October

ON OCTOBER AFTERNOONS you take your .22 rifle and walk away from the ranch house deep into the pastures — hunting perhaps, but more than likely just wanting to get the feeling that comes with being alone in the woods when the leaves are beginning to fall and there is a hard clarity to the air once more.

It is leather-jacket weather, though not cold enough to zip up. You wear your jacket loosely and open. The weight of it feels good — very comfortable against the brisk afternoon.

The woods have within them a mood of great silence and space, and the smell of damp leaves and trees, mixed with the sharp pungencies of your jacket and the metal of your gun, almost beg you to breathe more deeply — to know the land and the air a little more intimately.

In the clearings, reddish flint rocks lie scattered about like little oblong iron stoves, glowing with a roseate warmth that they manage to hold from the few pale rays of the overcast sun. And tall bare trees, post oaks mainly, stand around everywhere like groups of thin, work-hardened men who finally have a Saturday afternoon off but can't think of any place to go.

There are animals about — armadillos nosing along through the leaves, does and fawns that give just a single glimpse of themselves as they disappear down a hollow, jackrabbits that lie with their long ears flattened against their bodies and then race across the grass in frantic, dodging bursts. But mainly there is just you and the trees and the afternoon growing steadily darker and colder.

At twilight, when you begin the long walk back across the pastures to the ranch house, you become aware of an incredible stillness, as if all the birds in the world have suddenly died. And the air becomes immensely chilled — as though the coldness of the night has been lying hidden in the ground, ready to rise at the moment of sundown and go forth into the woods like some huge and rested animal.　　　　➴

In the Pasture

IT IS EARLY IN THE AFTERNOON, and Trinidad, the Mexican hired hand, rides in the pasture after goats, gathering them in for the next morning's shearing. It is a day when the sun is heavy on the land, and the air quivers in an invisible corrugated blaze. In the clumps of live oak, summer locusts make long, fierce cries of singing, sounding as if the afternoon itself has found its tongue and is protesting against the heat.

Trinidad keeps his horse jogging briskly along through the hot open clearings, heading to an outlying thicket of shin oak where a small bunch of goats stand hiding from the sun. The horse, a strong black one, keeps stumbling now and then on the flint rocks hidden in the needlegrass. Too, he is bothered by the swarm of summer horseflies that follow him in a small pestilent cloud. He bobs his head and switches his tail continually against them, but they just rise routinely a little ways from his hide and then settle again to draw out their many bright drops of blood.

As Trinidad approaches their place of shade, the goats watch him with unblinking, comprehending eyes. They want no dealings with this horseman and will not yield to him easily. Trinidad begins to shout and slap his hand against his thigh, but the goats stand unimpressed. They stare at him directly, the way a hostile human would. Trinidad takes off his hat and waves and shakes it at them, then he rides on into the thicket, bending down low in his saddle to avoid the branches, yelling, "Hey-ahhh, hey-ahhh," trying to intimidate the goats with his big threatening sounds and movements.

Gradually, as if after some brief, unwanted decision, the goats turn their eyes from Trinidad and begin to desert the thicket. Yet they do it with no air of lost pride. Heads up, austere, almost arrogant, they move along slowly and un-rushed, forming a single line behind their leader and moving silently across the clearing and then heading toward a new clump of trees and a new resting place. They hear Trinidad cursing as he sees them leave the trail and bed up in the shade again, but they remain calm. They are quite aware of the long ritual they must endure with Trinidad during the hot after-noon as he drives them slowly to the pens. With their un-blinking glassy eyes fixed in his direction, they wait: some chewing on their cuds again, some panting a little, but all uncompromising, all aloof — all goats.   ⇒

Aunt Annie

AFTER TURNING THE DINNER GLASSES upside down to drain on the white tablecloth, Aunt Annie would get her bonnet from the nail by the wood stove and leave her cool dark ranch kitchen and go work outside in her garden in the hot afternoon sun. She would gather snap beans with her German police dog, Tom, who moved along behind her in the rows like a detached but loyal honor guard. They both enjoyed the garden: Aunt Annie could do the small steady jobs of picking or gathering with her hands and still have her mind free to play among old memories (her mouth pooching out nervously, quickly, as it tried to match the inner rhythm of her thoughts, the many wrinkles around it working like a dozen drawstrings closing and loosening a tobacco sack). And Tom, though dutiful and companionable, could still sport along in the sun and find his own idle amusements in clumps of vines and good-smelling dirt.

They liked it there in the garden very well, even after Uncle Newt had died. They liked the sound of the windmill's endless and comforting afternoon music; the long tranquil calls of the doves sitting in the green pecan trees beside the garage; the sun glinting along the smooth top loops of the garden fence in a friendly intimacy.

That was a few years ago. Today Aunt Annie lives in a rest home in Fredericksburg, on a side street that is very quiet and still. But the stillness is not like the kind on the ranch. It does not calm and surround a person with peace but isolates and makes lonely. It lacks an essential warmth. Aunt Annie knows this, but there is nothing she can do because her children decided she was too old to stay on the ranch by herself. (Their constant cry: "But Mother, what if you broke your hip or got sick? You won't even let us get a hired girl to live with you.") So chances are she will spend the rest of her life on that quiet street, sitting on the front porch under a light blanket and watching occasional cars go by.

It would have been better if she could have died out there along Johnson Creek, in her garden, on some warm and friendly day after dinner when the cool water from the windmill

pipe was flowing down the potato rows and she had her apron full of squash or okra or peas. Then she would not have died among strangers but in her rightful place, still at work and useful, still alert to all the small magics she had known from her girlhood days: the breeze moving through the sycamore trees down along the creek, making their lazy, papery sound; the old brindle cat licking itself in the sun with long untiring sweeps; the single small distant sound of a sheep's bell coming from across the creek in the west pasture. And in dying out there, on some bright July or August day, Aunt Annie could have had the funeral she deserved: the mockingbird to sing a tireless, flambouyant song from its corner fence post, the windmill to turn out somber benedictive sighs all the afternoon long, and Tom to lie down quietly at her side and mourn.   ❧

Pet Lamb

❀ A BOY HOME FROM SCHOOL AT NOON is feeding his pet lamb. The boy sticks a coke bottle full of milk through the wire fence of the back lot and holds it while the lamb feeds — until his tail is jerking with pleasure behind little puffed sides. The bottle is soon emptied, and though the lamb begins to bleat in his injured, imploring way, the boy leaves him, waving the bottle at him in good-bye.

For a while the lamb remains there at the fence under the noon oak shadows, full yet disconsolent, waiting until he is sure that the boy has definitely gone. As he waits he briefly excites his tail to drop a few pills — then, abruptly and almost chastely, as if remembering his last act, he moves away from the fence into the hard sunlight. He noses along the rocky ground toward the chicken house, pretending at first that he is hunting something more to eat. After a bit he jerks up his head with an idea and walks with a rather purposeful gait across the chicken yard and through the chicken house door. Rhode Island Red hens jump wildly from their nests as he enters — flying against the walls and screaming as though they had been raped. The lamb goes on, paying them no mind, and begins to nuzzle in their cool mash troughs. As he munches he peers up at the row of empty nests — looking bright-eyed and immensely knowing, as if his whole rakish life involved quiet plunder and keeping his own counsel.

He comes out of the chicken house after a while, feels in the mood to lope, and does so. He runs and stumbles his way past the garage and enters a hoarhound patch below the cow barn. But the patch doesn't turn out to be as nice a place as he had figured. It is very sunny and the hoarhound burrs stick to the tender sides of his nose. After flapping an ear at a cruising fly he leaves the patch and comes back to his afternoon resting quarters, the slanted-roof tool shed next to the garage. There, in the deep shade, with a yellow ring of laying mash around his nose and chin, he settles down on an old towsack and begins to chew: vaguely sleepy, vaguely smug, wholly content in being a lamb.

The Bachelor Ranchman

W HE IS BEGINNING TO GRAY now in the temples, a lean bent-shouldered, almost stringy man with small high, flushed cheekbones that are like deep rouge spots from years of sunburn and heavy drinking. His tanned, tight-stretched skin is worn almost silky; and sometimes when the sun glistens on his face and hands, it is as though they are some kind of smooth, reddened leather.

His eyelids are heavy and slack, as if allowed to sag like half-drawn shades in a house of long sadness. The eyes themselves are soft and dark and quiet—finely set, with long lashes, seeming almost incongruously innocent in the midst of all the deep lines of his face and neck and in his tough, weathered ranchman's skin.

Standing on his front porch in mid-afternoon, rolling a cigarette and squinting out toward the pastures, he has a slender, still-handsome face profiled under his small battered Stetson. It is not the handsomeness of regular features, not just the shape of good bones and the right curve of neck above the collar. It is breeding and refinement that show in his face. He has the marks of a thoroughbred. And yet, as you watch him smoke his cigarette, watch him draw on it, the lean cheeks caving in slightly with the long puffs, you see something else too — the unmistakable line running through the breeding and refinement like mercury across a thermometer, the stripe that, according to how you read it, says character failure, or unhappiness, or waste.

Afternoon Wine

ONE HOT AUGUST AFTERNOON an old buck sheep stood
on a high ledge overlooking a stream. He stood motionless
and intent, with his massive head and horns turned slightly
to one side. He seemed curious about something in the scene
below — perhaps the glint of silver minnows in the water, or
a cluster of wild canaries flashing dramatically by. Maybe it
was just a mirage, a vagary in the heat-charged valley air that
arrested him. But regardless, he stood there on the narrow
ledge while long minutes passed, his head turned, his legs
planted solidly, his big unblinking eyes still staring.

It was just an ordinary stream below him, one with waters
that for the most part were quiet and unmoving — containing
only small waterfalls where muscular ridges of water flowed
together across smooth and glistening rocks into a lower, moss-
flecked pool. Along the edge of the stream a row of quite
ordinary sycamores stood spaced and tall, their leaves spread
like wide, anticipating hands toward the face of each gentle
valley breeze. And reaching back from the stream were just
ordinary grassy banks, full of yellow-and-black winged grass-
hoppers that rose here and there in brusque, snapping little
sails.

Yet who can say, really, what such a stream and its surroundings might mean to an old buck on a hillside — a stream
lying in the midst of so much bright sun and afternoon peace,
a stream that spoke with such a melodic gurgle and bubble
from its small waterfall? Perhaps to the sheep, isolated on
his ledge, the stream was like a skilled country winemaster,
gathering out of the valley all the tender grapes of sight and
sound and smell. The damp pungencies of watercress and
cool river shade, the papery touchings and retouchings of the
cottonwood leaves in the wind, the sound of distant mourning
doves — the river gathered them, crushed them into its dark

steady flow, and then, magically, released them back to the afternoon in the form of champagne — a sparkling afternoon wine that the old buck sheep could hear tumbling and bubbling downstream.

No one knows much about the emotional constitution of sheep — maybe they are just not made for such things as wine on hot August days. In the case of the buck on the ledge, it is probably safe to say that he overreached himself in his moment of contemplation and became heady. For after standing and looking and listening a while, he suddenly gave a deep buck-sheep cry of surprise and fell from the ledge into a deep ravine. It was exactly as though he had fainted. Tree limbs cracked and there was a scattering of leaves, and then — a long silence. Nothing could be heard except the river, still speaking quietly at its waterfall. Minutes passed, and finally the old buck arose from his thick bed of Spanish oak leaves. With a huge snorting and shaking of horns he slowly made his way out of the ravine and climbed back into the hills. ❧

The Woods

❦ IT IS TEN O'CLOCK AT NIGHT, and three hunters are walking through a hill country woods, slowly. The man in the lead carries a flashlight but he never turns it on to see by; for it is one of those nights when the heavy light of the moon lies across the land like pale blue sunshine, revealing outlines of trees and grass and sky but not the truth or comfort within them. It is as though the men are walking in a strange blue daylight, or across a dream.

The December night air is jarring cold, and though they are all wearing coats the three men walk steadily to keep themselves warm. Every now and then the man second in line passes a whiskey bottle in a paper sack to his two friends. They take a brief swallow, letting the whiskey burn down their throats and hit in their stomachs with a warming burst; then, satisfied, they hand the bottle back and wipe their mouths with their coat sleeves.

The man third in line, wearing a small black Stetson hat, started out the hunt smoking cigarettes but has stopped now. He has gradually succumbed to the mood of the night, to the strange, clear, day-blueness. He feels ill at ease smoking a cigarette without lots of black pervading darkness for it to glow in.

The dogs left the men long minutes ago, striking a scent, and they are now farther on in the woods, working. The men listen for them as they walk, and to the big silence of the surrounding land. It is a silence that seems to lay poised on the very edge of sound, ready to break open somewhere at any moment in a sudden small focus of maddened barking.

As the men listen for the dogs they smell the cedar trees deeply pungent in the cold woods and they continue to pass the whiskey bottle in its sack back and forth between them. Every now and then they stumble over unseen logs or stop to unsnag their coats from shadowed limbs. They enter into very little talking. Silently, in line, a small steadily moving troupe, they advance into the woods: walking down into the small ravines of the pasture and then up again into long flat grassy clearings; walking under bare post-oak trees with great extended leafless limbs; walking where hidden flint rocks lie scattered in thick needle grass and where every step must be taken with care. But though they do all this walking, steadily, without speaking, a place of rest for them never seems to come nor do they ever hear the dogs. The three men, in the heavy moonlight and the cold, just keep walking steadily forward into the heart of the woods.

Red Barn on the Llano

A YOUNG MAN stood on the edge of a bluff overlooking the Llano River. It was early, before breakfast, and the morning coolness gave the young man a sense of lightness and unused strength. He had on well-worn, comfortable khakis, pulled tight by his belt across a still-empty stomach. His face, just washed, was drying into a pleasant tightness in the steady river breeze.

He stood gazing down at the shining Llano that ran like a mercurial artery across the top of the land. Along its bank were strange reddish boulders that seemed to hint of prehistoric times — when great lizards lumbered out of the holes in the bluff to come doze in the sun.

Just across the river he saw an alfalfa field, green and level and trim. It was a calendar-picture field, the kind he had seen years before in elementary school books and that always made words like Commerce and Farmland and Labor rise majestically in his mind.

Then as the young man happened to turn slightly — so that he faced the far west end of the river where it curved out of sight — he saw a huge red barn almost hidden among the trees. It was a shocking thing, wholly out of place — an interloper in the greenery of the riverbank. What was it doing there, so obviously unwholesome and so suggestive of intrigue? On a morning when the whole countryside was awakening so normally, when even the air was still somewhat casually sluggish with the night's leftover dampness, what was this patch of brilliant, harsh, uncountrylike red doing half-hidden at the river's curve — so indifferent to its surroundings, so mysteriously smug and evil?

The more the young man stared, the more it seemed to him that the barn was inhabited by anarchists or maybe even trolls — some private and wholly alien group who had worked grimly all night long at a secret strategy or vice, so that the red glow of their effort now hung there like a warning among the trees: Keep Out.

The Sun Children

𝖂 WHEN THE DAY finally reaches its deepest mood in the hill country and begins to rest a little in preparation for night, it always gives a signal to the sun that she, too, can relax a few minutes from her long duty in the sky. She can settle out in the west and give her children a little freedom — twelve hours is a long time to be confined in that small bright circle.

So the sun pauses just before night and lets her horde of slender yellow children creep in from the horizon and spread out over the land. They come silently and joyfully, slanting their lean bodies across rocks and weeds and tree branches like long marine animals hunting food. They clasp the faces of barns and picket fences, hanging on in a silent fierce yellowness, and for a few sustained minutes the land is their playground.

Then their mother calls. It is getting twilight, she says; time to go. Obediently, on a soundless cue, the yellow children slip from their leaves and posts and hurry westward. There, on the horizon — in a hushed moment that the land strains to hear — they get back inside their mother and disappear below the rim of the earth, leaving the world drained of its color for another day and feeling very old and very still.

᠔

Home Country

❧ IT STARTS AT OZONA, with flowers along the roadside and the desert turning to tree-covered hills. Home territory — that Steven Vincent Benet-place: "bone of my bone." . . .

I came back to it one summer from the west — in June, after a month of soaking rains. Through Pecos, Fort Stockton, all the Texas desert towns, I had been content with sunlight and great quantities of space: I was still pleased by the western absence of things. But at Ozona the mesquites began — miles of them, fresh and green and shiny as silk, with the white-ivory blooms of Spanish daggers scattered through them like cannon bursts — and it was there, at the sight of greenery and hills, that I knew I was home.

For home country does not mean relatives, or city streets, or friends of the past. That is something else again: a world made by people, complex and painful. Home country is *country* — a place of rocks and trees and goats and sheep; of mourning doves and cypress-lined rivers; of hay-fields; of pastures.

(Pastures: To go into them as a boy — into the grass, the scattered flint and limestone rocks, the shadows, the leaves and dirt on the sides of ravines, the bare clearings, the green thickets — was to enter a beautiful clarity, a great sense of what was pure and real. I would walk through tall needle-grass — stumbling now and then over half-buried rocks — and when I rested in the shade of a live-oak tree it always seemed that each limb was hugely intimate, like a thought, and the tree itself like a family. I came to love trees — and summer glare, and fence lines, and cedar posts — the same way you come to love people.)

Home country, hill country, the whole stretch of familiar land: I drove past shin oaks standing in the heat like demure tree maidens, heads together, their feet lost in a pool of mid-afternoon shadow; and a rancher in a beat-up hat and faded blue denims, reaching down from his horse to loosen a goat from a wire fence; and a highway workman resting in the roadside shade. Closer and closer, a sweet-sinking into familiar things — and pondering them in the leisure of the passing miles. . . .

A windmill, say: There it was, mounted on its commanding knoll. How many years had it turned like an all-seeing eye above that same clump of ranch-house trees — a constant symbol of possessions and home to the ranchman riding horseback across his land?

Or rocks. Lying there, white as tombs, they represented all that was timeless and impersonal — geologic upheavals, erosion by wind and water — yet they did so in an entirely pleasant way. A rock in a pasture was not like a galaxy suspended in eternal night; it was a *human*-sized thing fit for both the hand and the mind. A rock, in summertime, was one of the beatitudes of earth — enduring as the trees, pleasing as grass.

Toward Sonora the mesquites gave way to live oaks and cedars — the tops of distant oaks looking smoky-blue in the four-o'clock heat — and the land was alive with the sound of birds. Occasionally a deer arched over a fence and an armadillo moved through masses of shadows and leaves. A white butterfly jitterbugged its way among wild flowers and across the green roadside.

Passing still another wooden pasture gate, another windmill, another rancher on horseback, I remembered a similar-looking pasture on my grandparents' ranch and a similar afternoon. It had been in early summer, with a breeze drifting in from the south, and Grandpa and I were out hunting the last of the goats to be driven home and sheared. I had gone on ahead down a long draw, and Grandpa had circled around by the fence. And I remembered coming out of the live oaks and deep shade and seeing Grandpa riding along the top of the ridge with the goats. They were a subdued little bunch for goats, following fairly well the trail to the pens. Grandpa was jogging easily behind — not exactly smiling, but it amounted to that: his hat was pushed back and there was a pleased set to his face. His free hand rested on his hip and a curl of sweated grey hair was plastered above his eye.

And although Grandpa was then in his sixties and had never before, to my knowledge, tried to whistle or sing a tune, he hummed all the way across that live-oak ridge. With the goats wagging agreeably along the trail and the shadows coming long and deep out of the trees and the sun lighting the tops of the yellow needle grass, Grandpa sat on his own horse driving his own livestock toward his own home lots — and was a very contented man.

Near Junction the highway cascaded through great stretches of blasted rock — naked white gashes of exposed limestone — and entered the Llano River valley. The Llano, first of the home-country streams going east, first to create its meandering Babylon of towering pecan trees and deep-green fields. . . .

I thought: Now I know why I am not a revolutionary—have never had the desire to kick over old, established things. It's because the hill country does not teach you the need for change. The land is always so satisfying that you want it to remain the same forever as a kind of handy immortality.

I watched a pickup speed around me and then turn down a narrow farm-to-market road. It sailed past sumacs and fence line and Indian paint brush and was almost like a fish sporting along in a sun-lit bay: trim, assured, wholly beautiful in its own calm surroundings, it obviously *belonged*.

Sure, I thought, that's the way it is: you stay next to the land long enough and you can't help but develop a natural kinship with it: you blend together. It's like the piles of brush out in the pastures: you look at them rotting there — simply, with a kind of bare, stoic dignity — and you begin to feel that somehow even they add to you, complement you, are an actual part of your life and meaning.

As I passed a house a blond, bushy-browed rancher's son was getting letters out of the roadside mailbox. He was still dusty from working with stock and I could almost see him as he had looked stomping around in a crowded pen: yelling and waving his hat at the bawling, milling cows, the dust thick and swirling and clinging to his eyebrows until they finally shone in the sunlight like the hairy legs of bees clustered with pollen.

. . . The lazy, hazy poetic sense of fading heat as the road curved leisurely through the hills. Small neat houses, butane cylinders, water tanks: they were stuck here and there in the green countryside like currants in a rich pudding. And everywhere the pleasant unobtrusive handiwork of people — gateposts, barns, small by-passed bridges from simpler times.

At Ingram I decided to leave the highway and cut across to my grandparents' empty ranch house before going on into town. It was getting dark, and the Black Angus cattle feeding on a distant hill looked like hatchet blades driven solidly into the ground. The road dipped first into low-water crossings,

full of the smell of walnuts and sycamores, and then climbed back again to the wide ranchland plateau.

I was just starting to open the gate to the west pasture of the ranch when I stopped and listened: a neighbor's horse across the road was moving slowly through a sudan patch, the bell at its neck jingling casually. It was just an ordinary hardware store bell, and the horse was a bony-ribbed old mare; but for a moment, with the land quietening, it was like the Angelus as I had always imagined it would sound in the countryside of France or Spain: patient and solitary, a reminder for those within hearing that day was about through, that people should lay down their work and start gathering close to home.

The porch of the ranch house faces south toward Kerrville and a line of faint blue hills. As I sat there in the early darkness, listening to katydids pulse back and forth in the surrounding trees, I tried to think a little about Grandpa and couldn't. I knew the *alive* George Duderstadt — the shape of his head underneath a hat, his gait in the worn, run-over boots as he half-walked, half-stumbled across the back lots. But this new one, the one over in the Harper grave, the one barely three years old: I found we had nothing to say.

And Grandma, sitting in town in her lifeless little room, a small grey-haired refugee from the country adapting, at eighty, to new town ways: she had surrendered the ranch too.

They were both gone now — the human trustees had finally loosened their grip — so what would happen to the land? What exactly *was* a piece of land anyway, I wondered — did it ultimately belong to itself? Should earth always return to earth after a while — for a period of silence and private growth? Did anyone ever have the right to claim a hill or a clump of trees as his own?

I thought of these things for a while — sitting where I used to sit so often as a child, where I had listened to the big grey doves as they perched in the live oaks west of the house and soothed the air with their gentle calls: I thought about them and then got into the car again and began driving toward home.

It was clear that people had caught up with me — had gradually begun to nudge the country aside. For five hundred miles I had been loose on the land and now it seemed only fair that I yield to the demands of my own kind: to family, duties, memories. After all, I was due at a house, not at one of the pastures. So as I topped the last hill I opened all the windows and barreled on down — the cool sweet cedar air in my face, the familiar lights of Kerrville shining below.   ⇒

IV

At the Ranch

Gram and Grampa

I : *Zipper's Backyard*

🌿 WE WERE ALL THERE in the backyard on those many childhood mornings, all gathered beneath the tall and sober post oak tree: Gram in her faded bonnet, stirring soap in the washpot, bent into the curve of her morning's work; myself, spraddle-legged on the whitened, ash-packed ground, playing cars and war and ranch; Grandpa — the sound of him — out in the west pasture on horseback with the Mexican hand, yelling over and over in his peaceful distant liturgy: "goooootie . . . gooooootie," calling, driving, urging the goats homeward to the pens; the big yellow mama cat, stretched out on top of the washhouse with her chin hanging indolently over the edge of the roof, her little pocket of a belly swelling out in its slow meticulous rhythm, her long marble eyes nearly closed but still keeping a bare slitted watch; and our inquisitor, reporter, and clown: Zipper, the collie, who made of every morning a dog-odyssey.

Except for Zipper we were all preoccupied in almost languorous private concerns. The morning would wear on toward noon and Gram continued to stir, Grandpa to call, the mama cat to doze and hang her chin. I continued to make trim winding roads with my sardine-can machinery and load and unload my acorn-cows and button-goats and rock-sheep. But Zipper stayed on the move. He seemed to have an artist's hankering to see everything that was going on and react to it. As flies swarmed in the dense, mote-filled light of the washhouse doorway, he would pause to snap briskly at them, as if suddenly deciding to take their swarming as a personal affront. He dealt with them in the spirit of righteous reprisal, like Don Quixote engaging and vanquishing a legion of small but dangerous windmills. You could hear his teeth clicking and see the flesh upcurled around his mouth. After a while he would move on, immensely satisfied with his behavior. Perhaps he would stand a moment in the coolness of the post oak, going back over this most recent triumph or perhaps older and even more enjoyable ones. Then, with no cause, he would suddenly and violently decide to inspect himself. Wheeling his head down and stretching out his hind legs, he would scratch and gnaw until it seemed as if he had finally decided to scratch and gnaw himself to death. Soon the spell would pass and he would rise, instantly alert, perhaps not pleased by a turkey gobbling too much out at the woodpile or by one of the baby yellow cats stealing with too much dramatic stealth across the yard and disappearing into the small fig tree just inside the garden. Sometimes he would be standing on the sidewalk that led across the backyard to the back gate and discover that several red Hereford cows were looking at him from where they stood at the water trough beyond the garden. Their looking and their chewing would seem so insolent that he would run to the end of the walk and be inspired to do some of his best barking of the day.

And sooner or later he would get around to his routine morning stunt: trying to take an unnoticed nap in the shady bed of four-o'-clocks that bordered the back side of the house. He was never successful. Gram would always look up in time from beneath her bonnet and raise her long threatening soap

stick and shout *Zipper!* and he would jump up guiltily and dodge along the side of the house to the back screen door. He would sit there on his haunches for a while, quite chastised, gazing out toward the lots with the posed innocence of a well-mannered schoolboy waiting his turn at recitation. But gradually he regained his composure, and before long his shaky nonchalance had changed into a serene benevolence, like that of an elder statesman who found personality differences mere pettiness and not worth his long consideration.

II : *Flyswatting*

Through the years Gram's primary concern was keeping the house neat and presentable for company, and daily she conquered the threats of dust, dirt, and wrinkled beds. But never was she wholly successful in mastering her arch-opponent: flies. As a boy I would see her start swooshing early in the morning, with a cup towel or the back of her hand — always in a general way at first, still restrained, as though hoping that if she did not fully admit their presence they would become discouraged and go away. But by ten o'clock coffee they had invaded the dining room in such numbers that she was forced to say, "Harry, I wish you would do a favor for Gram. Get that flyswatter down and kill some of these old *flies.* I declare, I don't know where they get in at but they just *take* over!"

As an incentive Gram always paid her grandchildren a penny a fly. I was glad to take the money but would willingly have worked for free. Prowling through the cool familiar rooms of the ranch house, waiting tensely for the flies to land, skillfully attacking, gathering up, carefully moving on — that was the real joy and lure for me. Sometimes I spent whole mornings in the kitchen-living-room-dining-room area, clutching the floppy wire swatter and an empty cracker box for disposal.

Flyswatting is an art, with different surfaces requiring different skills for killing. If flies landed on Gram's bed you stunned them, tangling their legs in the counterpane threads; then, with the edge of the swatter, you flicked them to the linoleum floor and finished them off in a business-like way down there. A fly on a glass offered a different problem, since you were unable to bring full power against something breakable. At best you could simply wave the fly away and follow it to another landing, always trying to coax it to some flat place — shooing, blocking, intimidating with your swatter, always feeling in yourself the stealth and cunning of an animal trainer moving a dangerous lion from stool to stool.

Generally, relatives made good surfaces but otherwise were not much help. When they wandered into the kitchen and attracted a few flies, they stood still enough while I crept on a chair and swatted at their neck or arm or thigh, but on the whole they remained indifferent to the total drama involved and their chuckles at my kills were always a little forced and patronizing.

It was only Gram, of course, who understood my dedication to The Cause. If I happened to see a fly on her while she was busy at the sink, I would yell, "Gram, there's one on your head!" and she would obediently freeze, bent over and waiting. She played her part without the least bit of condescension and would have something laudatory to say afterward — even if I had smashed the fly deep into her hairnet and made her

keep her pose while I picked it out carefully with a piece of toilet paper.

After a good morning's work I would put my cracker box on the cold woodstove and lay out the dead, usually around twenty or twenty-five. Gram would get her black silk coin purse from the dresser and count out the pennies, saying, "My, Harry, you don't know what a help this is to Gram. Everything just *feels* nicer without all those old flies around."

III : *After Dinner*

Many times after the noon meal was over I would go sit in the old green rocker on the front porch, my bare feet sticking out beyond the porch railing into the warm sun. With the ranch settling itself for the long afternoon, you could almost feel a curtain of rest drawing itself closed across the land.

I would sit in the rocker, looking out to the big clearing beyond the yard, then on past it to the low distant hills that on warm clear days made a bright blue-and-silver rim on the horizon. You could see very far to the south from the porch, and on such resting summer days your thoughts went moving out from your eyes in a great sense of ease and freedom. You could just let your mind float comfortably on the afternoon and the scene before you.

Along the west ridges of the clearing beside the water trough, the sheep would be bedded together in deep live-oak shade. They chewed and rested and let their ears flap occasionally at flies. Now and then their bellies would contract awkwardly during an attack of sneezing or wheezing and a head would shake itself violently from side to side, as though the sheep were saying, "Dang the luck! this old needlegrass sure does get up your nose and *stay* there." A few sheep always remained standing, chewing a little but mostly just staring out at the hot glare in the clearing, as if deeply puzzled at the need for so much heat and light right at this time every day. Usually it happened, too, that one of the younger, more disenchanted ewes would decide to follow the impulse of some vague, private inspiration and would wander casually from the shadows into the harsh sunlight. Bemused, she would get a little ways, then idly turn to look back at the rows of white, dispassionate faces chewing at her from their haven of shade. She would immediately realize her folly — like a swimmer out in mid-lake suddenly becoming aware of the distance back to shore — and, panic-stricken, she would bleat wildly and run back to the safety of the shade and the mass of smooth, comforting bodies.

Inside the front yard, there would be hummingbirds hovering at the mouths of water faucets, pulsing backward from the hanging water drops with a beautiful quivering nervousness. And ants would be crawling slowly up the sidewalk toward the porch in the solid glare of the sun. You could see them pause now and then, as if to wipe their brows and glance up sharply at the hot and punishing sky. Then, barely rested, they would move on with a heavy air of martyrdom. They always gave the appearance of pioneers going west, facing each crack in the sidewalk as a new crossing of the Snake or North Platte. And under the shade of the salt cedar, next to the garden fence, Zipper rested his long black nose on his forefeet, the air from his nostrils tunneling steadily into the loose black dirt. During the main resting hours of the afternoon his slant eyes kept closing in an air of tired wisdom but never for long. He was always reopening them to keep a steady languid awareness of the yard, like a Chinese storekeeper watching his merchandise on a dull day.

There would be long stretches of time when life stopped and nothing seemed to move anymore. The yard itself, like someone finally rid of too many afternoon visitors, seemed to relax and take its long-delayed sun bath. Then, like shock troops, a squad of wasps would sail around the corner of the porch and land on the two hydrants in each side of the yard. They would walk with a great militaristic flourish around the pipes and you could almost see them whipping swagger sticks irritably against shiny black boots. Several of them, lesser in rank, made repeated forays into the darkness of the hydrant mouths and brought back reports. They would all make a few more investigations — some inspecting the nearby grass, others tabulating, conversing, exchanging estimates all along the pipes — until, on a given signal, they would peel off melodramatically and disappear from the yard.

After a while I would hear Gram come into her bedroom east of the porch and open the dresser drawer to get her chap stick. I knew by that she was getting ready for her nap, for the first thing she did after finishing the dinner dishes was to come and open the old yellow dresser and reach in among the boxes of face powder and hairnets and packages of straight pins and get out the small green cylinder of mentholated ice. There always seemed to be a little fringe of roughness on her upper lip, and rubbing in the cool, soothing ice provided her with a moment of supreme self-indulgence. She would take the top off and hold it carefully in one hand as she rubbed; then, finished, she would replace the cap just as carefully and put the tube back into the drawer and walk away from the dresser still gratefully massaging her lip with her little finger.

This was all part of an after-dinner pattern on the ranch that remained the same, always, unless there happened to be company or it was Sunday. First the dinner table had to be cleared in the dining room and the dishes carried back to the kitchen, where they were washed and dried and put away in the big hanging cabinet; then the white tablecloth was taken to the back door and shaken free of crumbs; finally the broom was taken from behind the kitchen door and the dining-room linoleum was swept into shining blue cleanness again.

It was an easy matter for anyone on the front porch to keep track of the ritual by listening to the identifying sounds: the constant, monotoned ring of each dish placed solemnly on its proper shelf; the long empty whine of the screen door opening, the silence, the hard flat shutting; the broom knocking hollowly against the kitchen door as it was pulled from its quarters; and finally the strange, rather entrancing rhythm of Gram's feet: moving chairs away from the path of her broom in a steady, precisioned way, with no wasted motion, she had a one, two, three pause-and-sweep routine that was the combination of a slow-motioned tango and the aggressive little waltz chickens engage in while scratching for food.

After dishes and sweeping and the mentholated ice, Gram was ready for her nap. She would get her glasses off the fireplace mantel in the front room and wipe them clean on her apron and gather up her magazines or *The Upper Room* and come back to her bedroom and lie down, hoping for a good breeze through the windows. She always made genuine first efforts toward getting her reading done, but it was never long until the glasses had slipped down her nose, her hand — palm upward — was limp at her side, and she was asleep, *The Upper Room* making a slowly rising and falling tent on her stomach.

And of course there was Grandpa.

At some point after the dishes had been put away I would hear him cough on the breezeway: the full-rattling, after-dinner cough that never failed to come after he had taken out his teeth and rinsed them in the kitchen sink and had begun to gather up newspapers to take to his room. Whenever I heard it, it never seemed just an ordinary cough of habit or catarrhal. In the silence of the house and the afternoon it seemed to take on a special and significant meaning: it was a pronouncement, a commentary, an act of assurance

— all three. It said that this old man who had been head of his ranch for over half a century was still around and functioning. It said that once again a day had passed the halfway mark at the ranch and everything had gone off all right: once again Gram had strained the morning milk and it was sitting in cool crocks in the refrigerator; the Mexican hand had once again ridden the fences and chopped brush for the goats and doctored all the wormy stock in the pens; the hogs were fattening and the potatoes were growing in the garden and water was still coming up from the ground. It said that the dinner meal had been another good one and the little chores after it had been taken care of, and now once again the ranch deserved to relax until coffee time came at four. The cough went on to say that though drouths came and needlegrass persisted and windmills periodically broke down, there was no real reason for fear on the ranch. It said that even though Grandpa was getting quite old and was retelling his same familiar stories more frequently, he was still all right and thus the ranch was all right. And with a Mexican hand that was steady, and good whiskey toddies to warm up the blood, and a good nap each afternoon, everything would continue to be all right for a long while. Things could remain as they had always been.

I sat in the porch rocker on such afternoons, my feet out in the sun, listening to that cough and to Gram lightly snoring (*The Upper Room* going unread still another day) and to the Seth Thomas clock ticking gently from its place on the fireplace mantel. I could listen to all this, echoed in the steady creaking of the windmill behind the garden, and I could think: yes, the ranch, the other home of your life, is resting all around you now, with afternoon warmth and peace spread across it in thick slabs. And all you have to do is sit here, tranquilly, and just let the ranch come flowing into the heart of you and then, effortlessly, in return, let the love you have for it seep back out of you across the land, from your eyes and thoughts, from your very body. You can sit here and be privileged to know, definitely, right now, that there is something in life you love, something for which your love can be full and unqualified. You, the ranch, life, and love — a place, a person, and his emotions — all tied together and made simple, somehow, as simple and complete as a hummingbird that is poised for a suspended moment in time and space to spear a drop of water from a hydrant's mouth.

IV : *Summer Nights*

When the supper dishes were washed and put away and Grandpa had set the pie pan full of scraps out the back door for Zipper, we sat on the front porch and looked south to the darkness and the stars. Gram sat in the rocker, combing out her hair from its tight braids, and Grandpa and I shared the curved-back double seat.

Everything out in the night would be in an orderly flux and simmer. A bullfrog croaked now and then from the fish pond, and crickets sang in the garden. Katydids flashed peaceful electric signals to each other in the trees.

There would be stretches when no one spoke, when each of us seemed to be tempering himself more strongly in the night and silence. Grandpa became just the red glow of his cigarette and Gram the steady crackling of her rocker against the cement floor. Sometimes after one especially long silence Grandpa would cough deeply and lean forward over the railing and spit into the flower bed. Then he would settle back to say, "I remember one time in the lower country when Paw and I went up to Cuero to sell some hogs," and the tale of Old Times that had been growing on him in the dark would begin.

If it was a familiar and often-told story Gram would begin to rock faster until she would finally interrupt brusquely: "George! We've all heard that old story a hundred times!" And Grandpa, never insulted but instead quite mild and un-ruffled, would say, "Well, I reckon one more time won't hurt nobody then," and would continue. It would never be a self-glorifying story. It would be pure reminiscence, reclaiming the era of his boyhood when he and Gram grew up together on neighboring farms, and touched either on the gently humorous or the gently vulgar or a balanced combination of both.

As Grandpa would weave his way through long-passed scenes and revive shadowy, forgotten figures out of the turn of the century, it never failed that Gram slowed her brisk censuring rock and was lured back into the vaguely-sweet years of her girlhood and early marriage. She brushed her hair slowly in the darkness and forgot she was supposed to be aloof from the tale. Many times, if Grandpa failed to wrest up a date from memory or got a fact wrong, Gram was right there immediately to say, "Lem's *cousin,* George; it was Lem's *cousin,* not his *sister.*" Grandpa would pause to consider, agree, and then be off again on the rest of his story.

Sundays at the Ranch

❦   AT FOUR O'CLOCK the families always re-assembled around the dining-room table for coffee. The grownups, just arisen from afternoon naps, sat woodenly at the table and spoke with level sober voices — as though they were all joined in a sorrowful wake for their dear friend sleep who had just departed. They moved their arms and bodies with almost painful care, as if during sleep their muscles had not only hardened into hinges but had rusted as well. Periodically they would lift slow coffee cups, suspend them a moment near their mouths while making some mild affirmative or negative grunt to a question, tilt the cups mechanically to pursed lips, then carefully settle them down onto the saucer rings with a bare polite sound. After each separate rite of drinking, their bodies seemed to settle and sag a little in the chairs, as if waiting to indulge more fully, like indolent lovers, in the voluptuous caresses of Folger's coffee that would ultimately woo and awaken them from their long passiveness.

No one moved or spoke excessively for half an hour or more. During long silences, perhaps a sheep would bleat outdoors in the distance or maybe the windmill would give a creaking turn. Both the silence and the sounds made the world of the ranch seem very simple and still. Shadows had begun to form noticeably in the dining room, softening and deepening the corners, and the room took on a rich subdued tone, like that of a mahogany cave. The men covered their yawns and idly drummed thick, work-toughened fingers on the table cloth, while their cigarettes sent up hazes of smoke that hung in the darkening air like thin trails of phosphorous.

Finally, at some unspoken moment of agreement, a chair was scraped back, a coffee cup was touched to its saucer a final time, someone laughed, someone left the room — and coffee time was over. The four o'clock spell was broken, there was movement, the dining-room became lived in again. Doors slammed, someone was coughing and clearing his throat out on the front porch, someone was flushing the commode in the bathroom. The small sounds of the mantle clock and the sheep outdoors were lost. There was movement outward, into all the rooms of the house, into the yard, and soon all the chairs around the dining table were pushed back and empty.

Usually it was at coffee time that we grandchildren suddenly remembered that all Sundays at the ranch inevitably came to an end. Up till that moment we had not stopped long enough in our play to think about it. We had forgotten everything — that we did not really live there on the ranch, that we only visited sometimes, that we would all have to leave and go our separate ways at nightfall. When four o'clock came, it was like being drunk on play and being forced to sober up at the dining table on the grownups' coffee fumes.

After leaving the dining-room we would usually wander out to the lots for a last look around, realizing that everything was gradually being geared toward leaving, that pretty soon one of our parents would seek us out to say, "You'd better start getting your things together; we've got to be going soon." We prowled through the goat pens and loading chutes and tried to recapture the wild, eager delights of the morning, but it was never any use. We would be leaving soon and we knew it and there wasn't enough time to start up old enthusiasms again. So we just walked along, touching fence posts and dragging our hands along the sides of barns, more or less summarizing the look and feel of things at the lot, fixing them in our minds until the next time we would be back again.

We threw rocks at trees and cans. We chunked at roosters but even when we hit them, we did not feel elated. The roosters seemed to understand our lack of malice, and they made little insolent, threatening advances at us behind our

backs as we walked away. We went to the clump of small
shin oaks beside the chicken pen and rode the springy limbs
for a while, making them arc down toward the ground like
horses' necks. They bent obediently and we galloped up and
down, but they too lacked their old morning joy and we
jumped off, leaving them to quiver awkwardly behind us.

We walked the edges of the dipping vat beside the hog
pen, trying to generate a thrill at the thought of falling in and
getting the disinfectant all over us and in our eyes and maybe
even swallowing some. We dug at things half-buried in the
ground: small amber-colored bottles full of dirt and with old-
fashioned small-necked shapes; a rusted ice-cream dasher;
half a croquet ball. We walked out into the maize field beside
the Mexican house and looked a long while at the sky and
remembered the time that we flew a kite so high in spring.

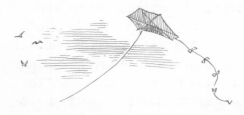

We circled through the lots again, throwing rocks at the hollow, orange-rusted water tank beside the corn crib just to see
who could make it sound the hollowest and oldest and most
deserted. We stood on one another's shoulders and lifted up
one of the tin windows of the shearing barn and stuck our
heads inside and looked at the quiet gloom and smelled the
onions spread out along the walls and listened to our voices
made strange by the emptiness around them.

Sometimes, as a last resort, we climbed on top of the shearing barn and looked west across the many oak trees and
watched the milk cows trailing home. Out in the clearing,

doves sat on smooth oak-tree limbs, calling in their gentlest, late-afternoon way, and there would still be a few sheep by the water troughs who had not gone on to eat in the pastures. Everything we could see and hear — the peaceful doves, the sheep, the rocks scattered in the clearing, the trees themselves — seemed to be marooned in a special stillness and quiet. The sun would nearly be down in the west and the yellow light of it was coming wildly through the trees, haloing their tops and scattering gold and red so harshly along the trunks that the bark actually seemed to be burning.

We would sit there, our arms around our knees, until the power of the scene had passed and the sun had disappeared below the horizon. Then we would climb off the roof and start toward the house, walking silently with our heads lowered and our thoughts turned inward, looking down at our curiously loyal legs and feet that had kept moving all day long without ever knowing it.

When it got almost full dark we would load things into our car and turn around in the front clearing so that we could wave a last goodbye to Gram and Grandpa standing together at the gate. We would see them still looking at us long after we had started up the road — until they finally accepted us as gone; then they would turn and start back up the walk together toward the house.

Inside the car everyone would be full of that big special silence that always settled on us after a day at the ranch. We would all look straight ahead, staring into the glare of the headlights on the road as if we were looking into a mild sun and trying to sear over the wound of our late Sunday emptiness and let-down. We listened to the sound of the motor the way bone-chilled people would seek out the warmth of a fire, letting it draw us together and comfort us in a way we could not do ourselves.

Enselmo and the Triplets

Ŵ ENSELMO, my grandfather's Mexican ranchhand, was the strongest man I ever knew. He could carry a sack of oats on each shoulder from the front-yard gate around to the cow lot and do it walking straight. He enjoyed doing things like that — carrying or pushing or pulling; he liked putting his strength to work. And he liked it best of all when he lifted cars out of ruts after a big rain. He would be milking or working around the lots when Gram — my grandmother — would send some of us grandchildren after him to go pull an uncle or neighbor out of the mud. We would follow him down to the long black mud flat below the house where everyone usually got stuck and we would watch him grab the back bumper and begin to strain himself with the lifting. We stood back under the live-oak trees out of the mist and drizzle and chanted, "Come onnnn, Enselmo . . . we're betting on you, Enselmo . . . come onnnn, Enselmo," and we would grunt and breathe heavily and get down low and pretend to strain along with him. And Enselmo would start shaking his head from side to side to show that if we didn't stop we were going to make him laugh and lose his hold. Then with the loose strap of his old aviator's cap flapping from side to side and the rain streaking down the smooth glistening black rubber into his face, he would set the back wheels down beside us on the grass and let out his big roar of pent-up laughter. For a long time he would stand there, shin-deep in mud, leaning back and laughing and showing his big yellow buck-teeth, looking as if he wanted to laugh so hard and so long that he would have to sit down backwards in the mud, too weak to stand, and give us all a chance to laugh that much harder.

Enselmo was about thirty when the triplets were born; Angelita, his wife, was just eighteen. They had been married four years and although both of them were crazy to have children, for some reason Angelita never could get pregnant. That was the year I was twelve and was staying out at the ranch on weekends, and I remember that at night when they would sit with us on the front porch of the ranch house Enselmo would say to Gram, "Oh, Miss Maggie, I sure do wish I had me a little boy — oh, I sure do," and he would put his big arm around Angelita and pat her to let her know that she was not to blame — that he was just sad she could not give him any little ones.

Then, as it sometimes happens, there was a shift in chemistry, a breaking of the spell — however such things are explained — and Angelita became pregnant. She was very sick in the mornings, Gram said, and I know that whenever I saw her, her eyes looked large and very black and tired. As the months passed and Angelita got bigger Enselmo would bring back little things from the pastures to cheer her up — a hummingbird's nest, shiny pieces of quartz, wild grapes. He was gentle with her, always opening gates and doors before her very carefully — even trying to walk a little more softly around in the house. But when he was out working around the ranch he was excited as a little boy. Sometimes I sat on the corral fence and listened to him talk to the cows as he milked them. "Hey, old cow," he would say, "don't you wish you going to have yourself a nice big boy, or maybe a pretty little *chamaca?*" When the cow would just go on eating in her feed box, paying him no mind, Enselmo would strip one of her teats extra hard and laugh — and after he was through milking he would kiss each cow lightly on the ear and then turn them loose into the lots with a terrific hand-smack on the rump.

The day the triplets were born Angelita's kinfolks came out from Kerrville and parked along the fence line between the Mexican house and the cornfield. Gram and Grandpa wanted to take Angelita in to the hospital, but the old women smiled and said something to the effect that they were very familiar with babies. I don't remember when the first one came — I was out hunting squirrels in the front pasture — but about nine that night Grandpa came back from the Mexican house and told Gram and me that the dam had broken — Angelita and Enselmo were parents of triplets, all girls. The next morning when I went up to see, they were laid out on a quilt, looking like three big shriveled acorns. Each had a thick wad of black hair — as though they even had on little dark acorn caps.

I don't recall exactly what it was that went wrong with the triplets — some sort of infection or respiratory trouble, or maybe they were just too small — but within a week all three of them had died. When the first baby got sick Grandpa wanted to take them in to town, but the old women just kept on fussing over them and making some kind of herb tea and saying that the *niñetas* would be all right. After the first one died Grandpa got a doctor to come out but it was too late; the other two died the same afternoon. The doctor told us that the old women just sat huddled over their knees, shaking their heads and saying it was God's will.

The funeral was held in Kerrville the following afternoon at three o'clock. Maybe Enselmo and Angelita didn't belong to any church, or maybe they were actually Methodists — but instead of being held at the neat Catholic cemetery near the Mexican settlement, the funeral took place at the small, run-down Protestant graveyard on the east side of town. It was Sunday, and when we got there a big crowd was already gathering. There was a row of Mexican men dressed in dark suits and they were standing beside their cars, holding cigarettes down by their sides and talking quietly. As Grandpa drove up they all turned to face us and the talking died away. I remember getting out of the car and noticing how still everything was — and how you could hear the short, almost polite sound of car doors being shut up and down the dusty country road.

The cemetery was full of weeds and yellow June flowers and dark places where the tombstones were hidden. We all walked through a gap cut in the wire fence and headed toward the middle of the field where a hole had been dug that morning. The Mexican women were dressed in black and seemed unusually small — strung out across the cemetery like little dolls of coal. The men had dropped their cigarettes and they walked along together. Some of them touched their hats every now and then to pull them down a little more the way they wanted them. We gathered around the hole and then turned sideways to watch the men who were bringing the small home-made coffin through the gap. When they got to the grave the men set the coffin down and then stepped back into the crowd. They carefully dusted their hands away from their suits and looked at the minister, waiting for him to begin.

Reverend Rodriguez talked first in Spanish, then in English, but I don't think I heard much of what he said. I kept watching Enselmo out of the corner of my eye. He stood there next to Angelita with the front half of each shoe disappearing into the caliche dirt and his body jerking as though he were standing on top of some kind of throbbing machinery. His eyes were squeezed shut and a row of big yellow front teeth was clamped down over his bottom lip. Every now and then little pouches of skin on each side of his mouth would puff in and out as air forced past them in explosions of crying.

The services ended and the casket was lowered and before I knew it we were making our way back to the cars outside the fence. I remember thinking as we walked along that the whole east side of town would have been quiet that afternoon if Enselmo had not been crying. He staggered along through the knee-deep weeds with Angelita gathered under his big right arm, and it was like a big shambling bear being led along by a child trainer. When they got to Grandpa's car Angelita opened the back door and helped Enselmo inside. They sat there together while Grandpa made his way around to the driver's seat. Enselmo had his arm in the window, holding on to the side strap, and you could see his big wrist sticking far out of Grandpa's old blue suit. When I got in the front seat he was starting to let low broken screams crawl around in his throat.

Grandpa asked Enselmo if he and Angelita wanted to stay in town a day or two with some of Angelita's relatives. But Enselmo shook his head and said, "No, Mr. George, we go on home." So we started on the twenty-mile drive through the heat — Gram, Grandpa, and I solemn and quiet in the front, Enselmo moaning to himself and his window in the back. Angelita just kept on being numb — almost wilted down inside herself, whimpering a little and twisting and re-twisting a white lace handkerchief around her thumb.

Since it was Sunday and there was no work to do except the chores later on, after we got back to the ranch Enselmo and Angelita went up to the Mexican house and I had coffee with Gram and Grandpa out on the breezeway. They sat in the green wicker chairs and began talking over everything again — going back to when Angelita was pregnant and how no one thought that a frail little person like her would ever have triplets, even though she did get so big; and how small and wrinkled the girls were when they were born — "just like little old possums," Gram said. And they talked about how pleased Enselmo had been all that spring, laughing and shaking his head in the happiness of Angelita's having a baby. Then Grandpa told again — though it was the first time I had heard it — how he and Enselmo had been out in the pasture riding fences back in April and Enselmo had spotted two baby cottontails in some brush and got off his horse and put them

{106}

inside his denim jacket and carried them back for Angelita. Gram said that Angelita had laughed and held them out for her to see and called them her babies.

And we were still talking along there on the breezeway — we hadn't even reached the midwives and funeral part yet — when we heard Angelita yelling as she came tearing through the back gate. Grandpa had got up — he was barefooted and was walking rather gingerly across the concrete floor toward the kitchen — and Gram was pushing herself up slowly from her chair when Angelita rounded the corner of the sleeping porch, waving her arms. She came inside the breezeway and fell on Gram as though she were a crying post and could hardly stop crying long enough to say that Enselmo had gone, had left the house and walked straight across the cornfield and disappeared into the west pasture.

I wanted to go with Grandpa but he told me to stay there with Gram and Angelita. He said he didn't think Enselmo would do anything "bad" — he paused a little before saying the word — but he ought to go take a look. He saddled up and rode off from the pens and stayed gone the rest of the afternoon. Angelita cried a while but gradually she settled into long after-crying hiccups. Gram made some strong iced tea and got her to lie down. Then Gram and I went out on the front porch where we could see the pastures better, and we waited. We listened to the cows beginning to low in the fields and watched the cardinals sail into the yard for their late afternoon dips in the bird bath, but there wasn't a sign of Enselmo.

When Grandpa came back to the house it was after dark. He said he had ridden all over the west and south pastures, calling Enselmo, but he didn't see a thing. Angelita broke down again and Gram got her to say she would spend the night at the ranch house so she wouldn't be so lonely. We all had a little supper and after doing the dishes sat out on the porch a while. Nobody cared much about talking, so pretty soon we came inside and went to bed.

We were eating breakfast the next morning when Angelita sort of yelled and then stopped herself with her hand at her mouth. We looked out the front door and saw Enselmo walking up the road from town. He was still a good ways off but we could tell he was carrying something on his shoulder — some kind of box. I guess we all knew what it was the moment we saw it but no one said anything — we were pushing back chairs and heading for the porch.

Enselmo carried the coffin as if it were just a short two-by-four — both shoulders were perfectly straight and level. When he reached the yard gate he bent his knees a little and opened the latch with his free hand and after carefully shutting it behind him came on up the front walk. He looked first at Angelita, then let his eyes slide on past Gram and me until he was facing Grandpa.

"I heard you, Mr. George," he said, "and I saw you, but I was scared you stop me. I was scared Angelita try to stop me too." And after getting a little better hold on the coffin he went around the corner of the porch. We heard the back gate slam and the cows bawl as he walked up past the lots toward his house.

We watched him off and on throughout the morning. He picked out a clump of live oaks down the fence line from the Mexican house and there he dug the grave. He covered it with wild flowers and then chipped out a small tombstone from a smooth caliche rock and engraved three crosses on it and placed it solidly in the ground. When he was finished he knelt down and cried a final time and then he went on back to the lots in his sweat-circled blue suit to help Grandpa with the chores. ≈

The Ranch: An Ending

◊ THE RANCH IS GOING NOW, as any living thing must go, and I am not sure what will come along to take its place. I believed, once, that such a passing would be entirely bad, and I raged and mourned in the same breath, just thinking about it. But now, with Grandpa three years in his grave and Gram sitting hollow-faced before the fire, I cannot truthfully say what I feel, for my grandparents were the heart of the ranch when I loved it most, and once both of them are gone I will not care, perhaps, to know it again.

During my childhood the ranch was many sights and sounds and smells, all in their proper places and never in excess — balanced, as the days themselves were balanced between work and eating and talking and rest. There were always the sharp yells of the Mexican hired hand working with goats out at the pens, and the hard bumps of the goats themselves as they ran frantically against the tin sides of the shed. There was the strong smell of soap cooking in the washpot under the backyard post-oak tree, and the scent of wet laundry in the peach orchard — coming faintly on the breeze like a clean-smelling bloom. There was Grandpa, with only the top of his old Stetson visible as he moved along past the board fences at the lots; and Gram, walking back and forth between the kitchen and the screened-in porch, humming fragments of a hymn as she set the dinner table.

The ranch was where life relaxed — seemed willing to breathe. It was where, in summertime, the mockingbirds sat on telephone poles like kings, and heat lay across the green rows of the garden in loving, shimmering waves. It was where I could be day after day without having a secret, gnawing desire to go to some other place. For whatever I needed was right at hand: a cool front porch to sit on if I grew tired or lazy, a slice of watermelon to eat if hunger spoke up too loudly before dinner time, back lots to roam through if I felt in need of mild adventure.

In summer, too, there was earth to touch — plowed clumps to pick up in a field, to crumple idly in your hand until they satisfied you by turning into warm, trickling dirt. There was a windmill to climb, wild sage to smell, an old truck to look at west of the house (seeming *good*, somehow — as though having a rusting green cab and worn upholstery and a scarred bed with wooden sideboards was actually a virtue). Sometimes after wandering across bright midday ground you went into the luring brownness of an open-faced shed and explored the strange and intimate dark. You could usually find a hen stealing out her nest in a corner, and the remains of an old broken plow.

And then always following the heat and exploring, a bath. You washed leisurely — the scent of Palmolive soap rich in the room — and afterwards, as you dried, you stood listening to the bathtub draining itself with its familiar Lewis Carroll words and voices: *barl, blouk*—the water went belching down through the old pipes; *platt, platt,* the faucet began a steady drip. And at two o'clock, as you listened closer, the whole ranch would seem to be moving at just such a *plern . . .* dar *lunk* bathroom rhythm, as though the very boards of the house were yawning and stretching in the lazy elegance of a summer afternoon. The peaches in the basket on the breezeway seemed to be sitting there at just this kind of pace. And Grandpa snoring peacefully through the wall; the fan slowly oscillating in Gram's bedroom past the kitchen; sheep snorting loudly and abruptly under the live oaks in the front clearing — all were in the same obscure but patterned ranch tempo, and all gave you a sighing contentment deep in your bones.

Grandpa never spoke about his own love for the ranch — not directly. But sometimes on Sunday mornings, while Gram finished getting ready for church and Grandpa and I waited on the porch, we talked casually and gently about things of the land.

You never talked hard or overly long with Grandpa. You simply stood there on the edge of the porch, looking out with him across the yard, and touched the outline of a subject with familiar, comfortable words. You drew topics from the interests of his world — rain or drouth or animals or how the pastures were holding up — and never tried to prove a point or uphold some idea you had about truth. For such conversations were not a flexing of egos. They were, instead, labors of love, essays in agreeableness. They were the rare opportunity you had to renew your covenant with the past, to take part in the simple ritual of bridging the years through old and tested words.

If it happened that Gram was still not ready after our survey of the yard and the times and the weather, Grandpa would stand silent for a moment and then slip into the groove of old memories. He would usually duck his head a little to one side — in a kind of involuntary twinge of delight as he previewed his tale — and then begin, almost shyly: "There was a feller who got married down near Nopal once and he still had trouble with wettin' the bed. . . ."

(I stood with a friend the other day, looking out into the pastures of the ranch, and as we talked we spoke of the dying-out of the old men who had lived on the land and who was going to replace them. "Who is going to tell the tales now," he wanted to know; "who will tell the young ones of the traditions?" And it was true: that our fathers, born on the land, had long before moved to the city and had then in turn caused us to be city raised; and that the old men who talked at night in the front-porch swings and who handed on the family heritages to whoever would listen — they had passed now. And there was not anyone left to take their place; their century was finally over. "Why," my friend went on, "already the people in my family are turning to me and saying, 'You were with Uncle Seth a lot; you heard him tell about the cattle drives, and the feuds, and the James River place. What was it that he said; what are some of the old tales?' " And there was genuine anguish in my friend's voice as he blamed himself: "I didn't ask enough or learn enough when I had the chance; I didn't listen to all I should. And with the old ones gone now the young ones are asking me — *me* — to make the connection.")

Grandpa always showed, openly and plainly, that the ranch was his life. But Gram had a pose of only being wearily tolerant of her lot and always managed somehow to find a little list of grievances and discontents. Partly she was just following the country woman's code that said you must, out of good manners, tend to belittle your own: your cooking, the cleanliness of your house, the temperature of your porch, the state of your affairs in general. Partly she was indulging in the petty grumbling that all rural people are subject to when they get to feeling cut off from the world and a little lonely. If possible, she would want to gain whatever sympathy she could from the visitor who — in finding the meal wonderfully cooked, the house airy and spotless, the porch unbelievably restful and cool — might thereby miss the hidden bothers that Gram felt were her daily crosses ("these old *flies* . . . I could just kill that fool pup for laying in my flower bed . . . listen to that icebox: it makes more noise than a thrasher . . .").

And partly she was always being caught in the bind which developed when her natural desire for praise ran headlong into the country ethic that demanded modesty in all accounts of one's doings (I remember the many suppertime conversations in which she and Grandpa passed in review the foibles of their various neighbors: no one ever came in for as much scorn as the "blowjack" — the pompous, overweening braggart). So many times she was forced to fish for compliments — to say "I sure made a bust on my ol' cobbler; don't eat any of it if you don't want to" — in order that everyone at the table would immediately look up from a second dish of excellent peach cobbler and deluge her with protests — would declare stoutly and at great length that not only the cobbler but indeed the whole meal was good, grand, sumptuous, out of this world.

I suppose the closest Gram came to being completely honest — emotionally, personally honest — was when she watered her flowers along the front-yard fence. She always watered in the late afternoon, just before supper — leaving the greens and potatoes to finish cooking themselves in the kitchen while she took up the water hose she had laid aside the previous day. I will see her there always in my memory, fixed in a kind of tableau: a full-fleshed, compact figure in a flour-sack apron and worn canvas shoes; her back to the rest of the yard, her head bent slightly forward in an attitude of close attention and thought. Every now and then, with a quick, determined pull of her shoulders and waist, she would jerk the hose loose from its tangled coil near the faucet. But even then she never really turned about. She kept on watching the little forced stream of water as it sprayed out from underneath her thumb and battered against the flowers.

She remained for long stretches at a time, unmoving, gripping the hose almost like some kind of weapon. She was obviously watering her flowers, giving them life, but all the while she seemed to be doing something for herself, too, something private: it was as if at the end of another long day on the ranch she was letting the vigor of the stream pull out her deepest thoughts in order to let them disintegrate harmlessly against the cannas and four o'clocks. Yet all that I, or anyone, ever needed to do was come outside the house and call *Gram!* — and she would turn around, instantly the familiar figure of a person just getting her watering done. Many times, however, I have wondered what might have been on the other side of that steady, tranquil-looking back while I was growing up — and who that woman might have been that so often faced her flowers in moments of privacy and yet always turned around to us simply as Gram.

Emotions: for years they have been circling above the ranch in a quite predictable way: serenely at first, in childhood, like the pleasant wings that float lazily high above you on a cloudless day; then, later, with more dark distinctness, clearly not mere wings but obviously birds of bone and feathers; finally — recognizably — buzzards. . . .

I remember one Sunday morning when I watched Gram and Grandpa get into their car and move off in a thin cloud of dust to church. I was standing on the ranch-house porch, seeing the old green Buick get smaller and smaller as it made the familiar curve around the big oat field and then finally disappeared into the line of shin oaks that marked the eastern horizon of the ranch. Long after Zipper had come back from the gate to lie on the steps, and long after the dust had drifted slowly southward over the front pasture, I stared down that curve of road, telling myself: You had better get ready. Someday there will be no grey heads framed in a Buick window — no grey heads, and no more reason for the ranch. Someday this corner of the earth will heave in an invisible little spasm, surrendering its old folks and its claim to glory.

I knew then, as I know now, the facts: that the windmills would find no reason to stop their turning just because one set of owners had gone; that the pecan and post-oak trees would keep on towering above the yards. Even the back gate would go on slamming with the old collapsing sound, no matter whose hand grasped it and let it go.

But the emotions — I knew them even better. I knew that they were deeply and unreasonably committed to the hundred and fifty years' worth of pioneer life that had just driven off to church. So, on the porch, I strove for a little wisdom. I told myself: All right, mourn this unhappened thing now; maybe that will help you later. Break the big dose into smaller ones and make it easier to swallow.

But I knew that was foolishness. I could not mourn on the installment plan; I could not get the jump on future sorrows. I had to just stand there — with Zipper at my feet and wisdom nowhere in sight — and do what I had done so many times before: look out across the ranch, searching it, hoping that something in the land itself would shift around and balance the uncomfortable weights I found within me.

Grandpa had a heart attack not too long after that (the same week my daughter was born: rhythm, balance? — such words have a way of coming around again to haunt you). He was in his eighties then and had broken almost overnight — his hearing, memory, and eyesight failing; his contact with the world suddenly becoming tentative and unsure. It was hard to watch him in his decline. . . .

There was one scene just before Grandpa died: I had driven

him from the ranch up to Harper, a little town nearby, so he could get some drench for his sheep; and afterwards, before starting back, we stopped at a grocery store-cafe to have a bottle of beer. That was one of the pleasant rituals he observed after the grandsons were grown: to stop in after "tending to business" and treat his company to a Budweiser or Jax. And it would have been fine again this time — despite his stumbling gait, his cane, his air of not quite seeming to know where he was or what was going on — except that he spilled his beer. Grandpa just couldn't see any more through his thick glasses, couldn't judge distance, and as he reached for his bottle he knocked it from the table. The woman behind the counter came over with her dustpan and mop and in her deliberate singsong way told him, "That's all-l-l right, Mr. George" — trying not to show what her mind was actually saying: "Umm, umhh, that old man . . . still drinkin' his beer when he can't see no more how to hold it or even hear the bottle when it breaks." I knew all the people in Harper could remember Grandpa from better days — before he had become so awkwardly old — but that didn't keep my insides from crawling as the woman patiently mopped the floor and Grandpa, his eyes hugely grotesque through the coke-bottle lenses of his glasses, smiled foolishly and apologetically and tried to tug his wallet out to pay extra for the trouble he had caused. I kept wanting the woman to remember Grandpa as he had been in his younger days — as I had seen him in the family albums. And as we drove home I kept wishing he could have yielded to posterity like that too. For with his Stetson hat, his black solid boots, his blunt toughened hands, it had always seemed to me — looking at him over and over in those old snapshots — that he would have needed only a slight injection of marble or steel to become immortalized into a monument: to become permanently transformed into the hard-creased prototype of Hill Country Rancher.

It is spring now at the ranch — not a traditional time of ending. Yet the ranch as I have known it, as it has known itself, keeps slipping away from the old forms into something new.

Even the habits of grass are changed. After Grandpa died and Gram sold off most of the stock, there were few hoofs left to beat the ground, so the grass started to grow where it had never dreamed of growing before. The woodlot back of the house — a place pounded for decades by milling herds of goats and sheep — has suddenly found itself covered by a spread of green. Looking at it, tender and quite beautiful — and remembering the woodpile and the great bare spots and the goats that would stretch all morning long trying to reach a single weed through the garden fence — I cannot help wondering where the lushness will stop now that it has begun. For it is not just in the woodlot. It is everywhere, and seemingly full of purpose — as if part of nature's silent reconquest of an old domain. It is like a graceful fungus, sweeping steadily out of the pastures, through the yards, over the house. . . .

Gram — she is merely sitting now in one place or another: when it is cold, before the fireplace in the living room; when it is pleasant outdoors, in the front-porch chair. I see her that way quite frequently: a small, grey-headed woman with her hands in her lap, letting her thumb flick back and forth against the rough, cracked skin of a worn finger.

I see her watching the sheep out in the clearing as they move toward the shade of the live oaks. She looks at them the way she has always looked at things — with her same old absorbing keenness, with that superb willingness to engage herself in any act of seeing or hearing. But though she does not miss a movement of the sheep as they walk, head down, toward the shade, she doesn't really see them any more. She looks very intently in their direction and then straight on through to where her thoughts are. And it is no feat to imagine what she is thinking — to know that she is saying to herself, as she has often said aloud: I want to see George.

As her thumb moves idly against her finger she brings to mind those mornings when Grandpa stood there in the clearing, studying the sheep — his boots dusty, his hat pulled low against the sun, his jaws working hard with the tobacco in his mouth.

George — the name hangs in front of her all the time now, a veil that prevents her from noticing things clearly any more; that keeps her saying over and over: I want to see him; I want to talk to him again. This old place. . . . ➤

V

Along the Coast

Galveston

ᐊ IT IS NO PLACE to bring fidelities, for at night the sky is too deep, too luring, and the air is soaked in too many coastal emanations and perfumes. The Gulf itself is responsible. It is so remarkably different from land that a visitor feels no bonds with it. And realizing this — the lack of kinship, of loyalty — the visitor is always led to think: Why, perhaps I have no ties with *myself* here; perhaps I could begin a new life. Perhaps a whole new Me is waiting, as strange and exciting as all this water. . . .

In that moment when he is first quickened by the dramatically spread ocean and night — by the unlimited blackness that seems to stretch beyond sight and knowledge — the visitor makes of Galveston a marvelous *Now*, and shrugs off the past as a distant, severed thing, only vaguely consequential. He is suddenly reborn. For him, only Galveston exists — it and the mysterious truths of its air and water, it and its dark promises. **ᐅ**

Corpus Christi

ᐊ ONCE, IN THE INNOCENCE of first glance, you probably saw a magic city. It was late at night, perhaps, in summer, and you were looking across spaces of wide black water to where Corpus Christi lay outlining itself with small bright

lights. It was all unknown to you then, this city; it was merely a shape of brightness, a phosphorescence on the edge of the silent water. And to the east lay the Gulf, stretched out like a huge testimonial to mystery and romance.

You have probably been in that city many times since then, but chances are its magic has faded to your eyes. The city is only real now; you know too much about the length of its streets and the shape of its days. The fact of it has laid its soul to ruins.

And so it is always with reality and dreams. In one's first glance — anywhere — there is never knowledge, only hope. A Corpus Christi, seen first in darkness and borne to your imagination on a coastal breeze — it is always your heavenly city, a place floating on a dark sea of timeless glory. Out of its vague outline of lights and moon-tinctured water comes the tune of all songs that you ever wanted to sing. But then, ultimately, there is that ragged trailing off of melodies, that gradual fading of rhythms — and all the dream crystals, stripped of sheen, lie hardened before your eyes.

Fisherman

 LOCKED IN THE STRANGLEHOLD of Sunday afternoon, tourists sat on the shaded porch of the Rockport bait house, drinking cold cans of beer and staring past the piers to the bay. The sun was still commandingly hot at five o'clock and the shade of the building offered deep and contenting relief. The porch was a place where you could back off from the afternoon and have your private thoughts about it.

There was no urgency in the air. Underneath the bait house, water lapped routinely against the wooden piles, and out in the bay motors purred dimly into hearing and then faded out again.

On one of the piers a big, one-armed man in a T-shirt stood fishing with a cane pole. He was staring far out across the water and paid little attention to the cork that drifted around below him. He had a leg resting against the lowest of the two-by-four railings.

After a while he laid his pole down and went into the bait house and returned with a can of Falstaff. He drank a long swallow, his shoulders jerking with a little inward belch. He seemed to come alive after that. He slipped the butt-end of the pole under the stump of his arm and held the Falstaff in his big, sun-blistered hand and stood rather squarely on his feet. He began to glance every now and then at his cork.

It was as if all that had been needed was some little good thing — like a swallow of cold beer — in order for the man to draw together the vague integuments of the day and make of them something he could endure. It was as though he were finally able to say: Shoot, let a man remind himself that he's just human and he can stand most anything. ❧

Crisis at North Beach

TWO MEN ARE in Rudy's Place at dusk, seated next to each other at the bar. They have been drinking since early afternoon. The one nearest the door — a thin, balding man with knotty veins protruding across his forehead and scalp — is leveling a finger at his companion and finishing a long pronouncement. The second man, who has kept his hat on, is looking deeply into his glass of beer.

"Now am I right or wrong?" asked the balding man. It is the Classic Question, as the man in the hat well knows, and must be dealt with soberly, with the help of the gods. He feels inadequate to the challenge — he has not even been keeping his strength up with the Polish sausages. So he does not reply but just stares a little deeper into his beer.

The balding man, though greatly encouraged, is still not satisfied; he wants an unconditional surrender. So he presses his attack. Leaning a little closer — his finger almost obscured now by his body but still pointing like a secreted pistol barrel — he asks again, with blurred rhetorical viciousness: "Sam, God dammit, am I *right* or *wrong?*" He keeps his body taut, waiting, and then gradually relaxes onto the center of the stool. He did not expect an answer and did not get one: the day belongs to him, obviously. As the bartender moves slowly toward them with a wet bar rag and two more beers the balding man waits for him with a victor's defiant air. The man in the hat sits staring into his empty bottle, shattered.

Coastal Sunday—or Seven Characters in Search of Nobody in Particular

TIME: *about dusk on a hot Sunday afternoon in summer.*

PLACE: *a small grocery store serving also as a beer joint and occasional cafe in a small fishing village near Riviera on the South Texas coast.*

CHARACTERS: GLADYS, *who runs the place whenever Joe is out;* IRENE, *a fat woman who sits with her husband* CHARLIE *at the table nearest the window fan; The* OLD DEAF MAN, *who sits reading a newspaper; and later,* JOE *himself, as well as* CURLEY, *a mild conversationalist, and The* SILENT SQUAT MEXICAN.

GLADYS: Inexplicable to you, the onlooker; either a little drunk or neurotic or mildly loony — that, or simply by-passed by life and vaguely knowing it. The central character of the scene, perhaps placed here by Tennessee Williams to let her grow more fecund until he decides to write a play about her: a barely sketched-in background figure dropped at the last minute from *Streetcar*.

As she waits on the tables she exudes that special something which is meat and potatoes to Southern writers who specialize in decadence and grand histrionics and women with minor-key, Helen Hayes voices who run thin fingers over cobwebs or silk and have an in-touch-with-fantasy stare. Like her more publicized sisters in fiction, she is in perpetual reaction to ennui and disenchantment — those two major thematic crops raised along Southern seacoasts. She is Lone Imagination at Work, shaping intense, arresting reflections from grains of salt spilled on a checkered tablecloth or the sound of her loose sandals flapping as she walks across the floor.

Occasionally you will see her stop in the middle of reading her newspaper and, with eyes transfixed, begin to Listen and Consider, like Julie Harris in *A Member of the Wedding* watching the screen door at night as outside moths batter against it in an exotic futility. (Gladys, the fascinating ambivalent: simultaneously vague and intense, a lunatic-saint preoccupied with visions. Like a gentle sieve she strains the vacant Sunday atmosphere of the grocery store, hunting for oddly shaped thoughts which she can ponder and caress, the way she would handle curious seashells while out for a stroll along the shore.)

When Gladys is not serving beer to the tables or standing in the doorway — caught in some private reverie as she stares out toward the bay — she sits at the counter on a high stool and reads a week-old Sunday paper under a small dim overhead bulb. She puts on thick brown horn-rimmed glasses for reading and presses them hard against her temples with the flattened palms of her hands. The glasses change her appearance and make her appear quite the sober citizen: a member of the Dallas Civic League going over committee reports. As she bends down over the paper, studying it, she muses aloud over the ads: "'TIRED BLOOD' . . . Charlie, *isn't it funny* the way you spell 'tired'? 'T i r e d'" . . . As she gazes past the top of the newspaper she takes off her glasses and begins to chew reflectively at one of the earpieces.

Whenever someone is ready for another beer Gladys slides off her stool, gets a Falstaff or Pearl from the ice box behind the counter, and goes over toward the table quite tranquilly, wondering out loud how big earrings should be and swishing along in her open sandals and flowing Spanish-style skirt. But along the way she sometimes undergoes a sudden private crisis: perhaps she has a violent recollection of some threatening moment in her past, perhaps she just remembers an old irritation. But her casual idling talk abruptly becomes explosive, and gripping the beer bottle at the neck like a dagger she begins talking furiously to the window fan or Charlie's wide back or the spreadout newspaper screening the old deaf man.

No one seems to pay her any mind, and the mood eddies and flows away, leaving her standing there in the center of the store like a well-wisher puzzled at the sudden departure of a ship, the beer bottle in her hand descending slowly to her side in its useless and unseen farewell.

JOE: He comes silently into the store and walks behind the counter, speaking to no one and seeming to watch the conversations across the room with a detached, unconcerned air. For some reason you wonder if he has ever killed a man, for he is somehow too mild and silent and opaque. He suggests something pathological. He either stands there behind the counter, not looking directly at anyone but nevertheless quietly alert to all the needs of the customers at the tables, or he moves about doing small managerial things — laying a pencil closer to an order pad or making brief unnecessary wipes with the counter rag.

Occasionally he comes from behind the counter and unobtrusively removes beer bottles from the tables. He gives the impression that he is purposefully and decorously not listening in on the table conversations, and you wonder if this attitude is fake — if he isn't catching it all as anyone else would. And then it strikes you: he really *isn't* listening because he isn't interested. All along he has been deceiving customers into believing that he is discreet and professional-acting when actually he just doesn't care about them.

This puts you to wondering again if he hasn't killed somebody once and is going straight now — maybe living under an assumed name here on the coast and being quite willing to let other people alone if they will do the same for him. Surely, so quietly moving and so detached a man as he has had a past and a passion. You try to visualize those outbursts of fury that inevitably must get out of control at times: perhaps Gladys is his wife and perhaps every now and then he uses his pocket knife to cut her up good on the wrists for some disobedience, or blackens her face with his small white fists.

You can see him at home some night, catching Gladys sneaking beer after he has told her to lay off: catching her at the ice box and slamming the door on her hand and holding it shut with his knee while she screams and he slaps her. Then after it is all over perhaps he goes along quite peaceably for a while, very much the efficient, small-time business man, making necessary corrections in the grey ledgers when Gladys rings up the wrong amount for beer, wiping the tables carefully and thanking the customers genuinely and courteously for the Alka-Seltzer and razor blades they buy. Surely the customers think highly of Joe and always have a good word to say about him.

He stands behind the counter, his hands resting lightly on the oblong chewing-gum jar. He seems ready for something to happen, poised like a decoy in a bank holdup. His hair is neatly barbered in the old John Held style but with no greasy shine or slickness. It is very full and parted close to the middle and is utterly black. His face is chiseled and pale and somehow seems vaguely foreign. He is not handsome but only because he seems too wooden, too much like a mannequin. And his body — it is almost too spare, and his clothes almost too neat. It seems as though he might not have certain glands functioning properly. Perhaps he has never been able to sweat or cry.

THE OLD DEAF MAN: He sits at a table reading part of last week's Sunday paper. He wears a small ivory earphone, with a wire coming down from underneath his olive-drab engineer's cap. He has wide suspenders hitched to stiff and starched khakis that fall straight as the face of a cliff down his legs when he stands up: he seemingly has no rear end at all. His face is brown and shrunken and leathery, and he wears steel-rimmed glasses. Now and then he lays the newspaper down on the table and gives a huge, conspiratorial grin as he shares with himself some secret mirth.

After a while he gets up, eases his chair back carefully, rolls his newspaper into a neat bundle, and tiptoes over to the counter where Gladys is reading. He stands behind her stool a moment before softly reaching across her shoulders with the newspaper and slamming it into the face of her comic section. Then he steps back, laughing silently at the back of her head. Gladys does not bother to turn around.

He goes over to a row of dusty shelves beside the counter and squats there on his hunkers, looking at the used, dusty pocketbooks that are stacked in among the canned goods. He studies the shelf, then rises and tiptoes from the store; in a few moments he returns from a shack across the street with five pocketbooks of his own. He exchanges them for five on the shelf, walks over behind Gladys again and hits her lightly on the head with the books, and then steps back, again hoping and waiting for her to turn around. She does this time and makes as though she is going to hit him with her glasses. This is what the old man has been hoping for, and he doubles over in glee. In this hunched-over way he leaves the store with his pocketbooks clutched in one old gnarled hand, still shaking his head from side to side with noiseless laughter.

And there are these, also:

IRENE: who has been in front of the window fan all afternoon, facing the counter and drinking her countless beers. She is a big Okie with a bland brown shining forehead and huge white buck-teeth that are so very white and so very buck that they seem to be false, made out of paraffin. She has cropped black hair, tinged at the ends with grey. Periodically she leans her great bulk back in the chair like an asthmatic hippo rearing up out of the water for air. Looking at her, you wonder if she was born by normal processes or simply proliferated there in the chair, perhaps from spilled beer, and was incubated into enormity by the constant generative whir of the window fan.

CHARLIE: Not a true florid type, but big and talkative. He would talk even more if he felt less awkward with words. He does not know how to make his thoughts and words precisely coincide; and besides that, he stutters. He has the manner of an oil-field roughneck who has worked his way up from the ranks to a small position of authority. He likes to laugh a lot — likes to feel the pleasure that laughing gives him — but Irene doesn't think any of his jokes are funny. When the young man named Curley gets out of his bread truck and comes inside, Charlie waves his beer bottle in a greeting and calls out in a loud voice: "Hey, C-Curley, you know what makes a w-wildcat w-w-wild?"

THE YOUNG MAN, CURLEY: He has brown hair growing neatly in the garden on top of his head. He is raising a fine crop — the convolutions are like tender brown cabbage or lettuce leaves. They are obviously well regarded and well tended and they shine with health. He wears brown Shinola-polished shoes and a neat sport shirt open at the neck. He sits at Charlie's table and laughs politely at Charlie's jokes while he gazes about the store.

THE SILENT SQUAT MEXICAN: No one saw him come in. He stands at the counter, one foot resting on the bottom rung of a nearby chair. He remains motionless and solitary, uninvolved in the grocery-store talk as dusk finally wanes and passes on into night. You are not able to tell whether he has drunk one beer or fifteen since he first came in. It is somehow never noticeable when he orders or when he drinks. He always seems to be staring straight ahead into the bags of Fritos and sticks of dried sausage.

Since nothing ever happens to disturb the hot, moist, almost greenhouse atmosphere of the grocery store-cafe, it would not surprise you at all if the body of the Mexican man — grown brittle from underuse — would slowly begin to fracture and fall away to the floor like pieces of brown plaster, until perhaps only the hand with the beer bottle and the leg jutting from the chair would remain hanging in the air. And you think that it would be pretty good if such a thing actually occurred: the two oddly petrified relics of the Mexican man, along with the mummified figures of Irene and Gladys and the rest, would provide just the right intellectual challenge to a future mood-archeologist pondering the remains of late coastal Sundays.

Waiting for Dinner

꩜ IT IS SUNDAY DINNER TIME on the farm near Robstown, and while the women finish getting the meal ready in the house the men bring their chairs outside and put them on the pale-green carpet grass underneath the front yard mesquites. They sit there for an hour or more, smoking, looking out into the bright South Texas noon, talking country talk in the mesquite shade.

In one corner of the yard several young cousins stand a good ways apart, playing catch. They face each other rather stiffly, with the special, sober formality of family get-togethers. They don't throw or catch nearly as well as they can at more natural times. They miss frequently and have to chase the ball over to where the men are sitting in the chairs. When this happens one of the men casually moves his leg or tilts back his chair and then, giving but one brief uninvolved glance downward to where the boy's hand is reaching, he goes ahead to scratch himself gently in the crotch or ribs and settle himself again to the easy mesquite-shaded talk.

Next to the porch steps on the concrete front walk a small, pretty, fat baby sits spraddled before a fox terrier, playing. He waves his hands vaguely in the air before his face like antennae, and the fox terrier occasionally ventures bold yet shyly self-conscious licks into the baby's face — very careful, tender licks, as though he knows exactly what a strange and marvelous and helpless thing a human baby is.

Outside the yard, on the top of a telephone pole, a mockingbird lets bright twisting scraps of song flow from his throat. He is almost like a vocal kaleidoscope, using snatches of varied and colored sound in place of glass. Sometimes when the mood strikes him he rises above the pole in high elegant jumps, sustaining himself in the air on balancing wings almost like an African ceremonial dancer strutting and leaping grandly about in ostrich feathers.

Away from the house, cotton fields are spread out like mild green lakes, and midday heat hovers closely about them in an almost masculine anxiety — as if the green planted rows are harems of vulnerable women to be guarded fiercely from an enemy world.

The noon wears on, and in the yard the men continue to speak their dinnertime words about cotton prices and Mexican laborers and politics with the same measured ease as the mesquite limbs above them move their long yellowish beans in the mild May breeze. They sit with comfortably crossed legs, their polished boots curving up in solid and restful arcs like dark shining scimitars. Those who smoke continue to hold their cigarettes and cigars down close to their chairs — and periodically, like indolent spiders moving about on a web, their fingers perform a kind of tentative dance as they join for a moment to idly flick the ashes away.

No

IT WAS A TYPICAL SOUTH TEXAS NIGHT — vacant and huge, with darkness and heavy warmth drawn like a languid curtain across the land — and a few cars had stopped for beers at a small highway cafe. Several men sat inside at the tables, talking; a couple of Mexican braceros in old hats and denim jackets stood in front of the doorway, smoking and waiting for the bus to come along from the Valley.

A young man and his girl remained parked in their car outside the cafe. They were not talking. The young man drank coffee while the girl sat slumped against her door, looking out at a mimosa tree that grew at the corner of the cafe. She reached her hand out the window once toward the tree, as though to touch it, but the tree was too far away. She let her arm die slowly against the side of the car.

The young man watched her as he drank his coffee. Finally he lowered his cup and looked out his own window at the highway.

"Look," he said, "you want to split a beer? Just one very small beer? This really *is* rotten coffee. And I promise: only one this time. One and no more."

He looked at her and waited, but the girl didn't make a reply. She still faced out her window, toward the mimosa tree. Finally she turned and looked at him and then she let her head drop back against the seat. She began to shake her head *no,* rolling on her neck back and forth across the top of the seat. It seemed the last and only thing in the world she wanted to do.

The young man looked at her and left the car with his coffee cup and went inside the cafe. When he returned to the car the girl was huddled down against her door, quiet but not crying. She still had not put her lipstick back on.

The young man did not look at her anymore. He tilted his beer bottle, taking very small sips, and watched the summer bugs crowd against the one lone bulb above the door of the cafe. Across the highway in the bar ditches, crickets sang steadily from their weeds. And every now and then the heavy monotony of the night was broken by a car passing by, going south in the darkness toward Mexico.

Virility: Bewitchment

THE YOUNG SOUTH TEXAS RANCHER waited with his trained fighting cocks, one under each arm, until his friends from Alice and Kingsville had gathered around him in a circle beside the barn. Then he put the cocks on the ground and stepped back.

As they fought he moved about them with his muscular, unhurried step — casually, the way a rodeo performer walks away dusting his hat after he has successfully ridden a brahma bull, or the way a high-school football hero leaves the downtown drug store on the Saturday morning after a big game. He moved as though his body were a hugely estimable thing — comparable to a cloud moving along in the sky or one of the seasons changing.

He stood there in the clearing, saying nothing, charging the cock fight with the tension of his bullish silence, using it almost as a tangible force the way someone else would use fists or words. And though his manner bordered on a kind of

laziness, it was the restrained laziness of a well-fed lion moving idly about. His heavy shoulders and thighs seemed to swagger inside his body, in a careless sloshing about of weight and bulk. He had a match in his mouth, and as he watched the two cocks he lolled it vacantly with his tongue. He was so full of nonchalance and self-assurance that he seemed ready at any moment to lift up his boot and rest it against thin air, the way he would indoors against a chair rung or the railing of a bar.

Suddenly, without any apparent cause, he spat away his match and reached down and grabbed both cocks, mastering and quietening them in the same instant. Neither one of them had decisively beaten the other — perhaps he was just piqued at some flaw in their performance. He opened the barn door with a single quick movement of his knee, went inside, and then pulled the door shut after him by reaching back and hooking it with his boot.

Maybe what seemed to happen next did not really occur at all. It had been a long hot Sunday afternoon, with the drifting hours falling away into a kind of lazy vagueness and unreality — so maybe the group of friends just imagined it. Maybe they just succumbed to an August illusion created by too much heat and Carta Blanca beer. But several of them swore it happened: that they were staring straight at the closed door when they saw the whole barn begin to tremble and rise from its foundation — like the cyclone-lifted farmhouse in *The Wizard of Oz* — and then fly with theatrical slowness out of sight beyond the trees.

Those who were bewitched the strongest say that they could not only follow the barn out of sight but could also see right through the door — could see *him* standing there behind it, one cock resting under each arm, a new match lolling under his tongue. He seemed wholly unconcerned, just waiting patiently for the barn to land.

Well, they say, it did land — far off toward the Gulf in a mesquite and chaparral clearing. But when the barn door opened and the young rancher stepped out, he emerged not with the two cocks but with two beautiful young women — each of his huge arms circling their slim and graceful waists. And though his friends at the ranch kept straining their eyes eastward, that was all they could see — just the three figures walking away into the brush with the coastal twilight beginning to settle about them in an almost magical swirl. ❧

Highway, South Texas

❧ IT IS MIDDAY, in spring, and along the highway from Alice to Laredo there is heat and a skyful of bright light and no end to the sweep of the land.

The leaves of roadside mesquites hang brilliantly long and green — almost poised, like fingers of a slim lady's hand. In the distance, beneath still other mesquites, a whitewashed mud house stands in a bare brown yard, shadowing a few bantam chickens and a Mexican child or two.

The land, vital from recent rains, is heavy with the smell

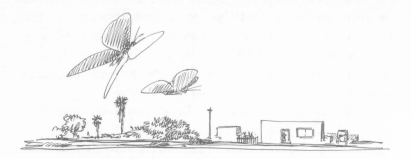

of greasewood and sage; the heat waves low in the air almost seem to be burning the green-smell as a desert incense.

Here and there wine cups quiver spiritedly in a breeze: colorful little Foreign Legionnaires outposted in the roadside sand.

And caught against the blue air of the sky like two artfully pasted stamps, a pair of white butterflies hang beside each other in a long moment of suspended grace and then, for the same unknown reason they joined, split apart — vanishing like smoke into the noonday glare.

Nighttime, a Park, and a Train in the South

SMOTHERED LAUGHTER comes from the little park along the railroad tracks in Kingsville. A voice says Shhh! — a girl's mild, ineffectual little caution — and then another voice laughs: a short, open, male laugh that hits the night and glances quickly away, lost in the darkness and silence. More suppressed giggles come, then pauses; finally two slowly lengthening shadows move from the solid blackness of the trees toward the railroad station.

The palm trees along the tracks flap in a brief rise of wind coming in from the coast. They are like long-legged birds stretching and ruffling their feathers in a fitful sleep. As the breeze dies, the palms are quiet again. The park lies still and dark except at its eastern edge, where patches of pale fluorescent grass shine beneath the lamps of the station. No one can be seen after the couple leaves except an old Negro man who sits at the far end of the loading platform, his legs over the edge. He sits there in the half-shadows of the building, smoking and looking south.

For a long while the night is silent. Nothing sounds, nothing moves. Then, quite gradually, there come from the south the first bare noises of the 10:40 train. They are subdued, toy sounds, mere hints at first, and the old Negro doesn't bother to look up. It is as though the night is what he is still listening to, is what is still powerful. The 10:40 train is beyond the night, its force capsuled out there on the edge of town.

But the train comes on, the sounds of it swelling until finally there it is, undeniable: its light swinging and jerking along the tracks like the lone eye of some enraged minotaur bellowing into town: coming, coming on, with a great maleness, making furious deep running sounds, hollowing into the tranquil silence of the night with the sonorous monotones of its loud blunt horn.

Sharlot

✿ ON THE LAST SATURDAY MORNING before she returned to
college Sharlot got into her Uncle Emmitt's old red pickup
and went into Kingsville for groceries. She always enjoyed
the short drive up the highway from the farm, the chance to
fade into herself for a while but still keep moving. She even
liked the bounce of the truck and the clattering of the old
motor — they gave her thoughts a kind of pleasant texture and
background. Surrounded by jostles and roars of the cab, she
could drive along, relaxed, not having to bother with thinking
up ideas big enough to compete with the hugeness of the day.
She could just sit there, holding on to the worn, throbbing
steering wheel, and let her mind idle among familiar reflections.

As she rode along Sharlot looked out her window at the
telephone poles beside the highway. How orderly they went
by, she thought — everyone in its place. She could not conceive of a better arrangement for telephone poles: each in
line with its neighbor and helping make a pleasant configura-
tion to the eye, each a neat Saturday-morning reminder of
how right things were in the world.

Beyond the telephone poles, far out in the fields, she could
see the cotton pickers bending low in the South Texas heat.
And with the big trucks loaded with cotton and the wide
coastal sky arching behind and the Mexican men scattered
through the greenery like figures on a lush chess board, the
scene reminded Sharlot of paintings she had seen illustrating
poems: the ones that showed laborers toiling in the sun and
pointed up the nobleness of their work. As she watched from
her pickup window the figures *did* seem noble and the scene
was like a painting — and she drove on down the highway
feeling a kind of pride in the fact that men had always managed to represent so truly the experiences of life.

Everything about the morning seemed to please Sharlot: the cats roaming with their nice casualness in the Johnson grass along the road, the sun shimmering on the tops of cars parked in farm driveways, the Gulf clouds drifting inland like slow heavenly dirigibles on patrol. When she reached the stop signs in town and listened to tires squalling a little on the hot pavement, Sharlot liked the thoughtful, cooperative people who applied their brakes so carefully. And the old men who sat on benches outside the railroad station, getting a little sun — they pleased her too, and she would have smiled at them from her cab window if they had ever looked her way. At the grocery store where her family traded, she even liked the brisk young clerk who whistled jauntily as he pushed his empty cart through the swinging doors behind the meat counter: who had on a clean tight apron and a pencil behind his ear and an air that seemed to say, "Shoot! It's not bad, you know, just working along and being alive."

Sharlot liked them all: people who drove their cars sensibly, people in clean aprons who whistled, people who smiled back when she smiled — everyone who looked happy and busy and seemed to enjoy being that way. They told her what she very much wanted to hear: that things in the world were all right, really; that life was orderly and friendly and good-natured; that God was good. She wished that every day was Saturday morning so she could have the roadside and the people in town to demonstrate their truths to her. She wished she did not have to go back to college where everything seemed to get mixed up, but instead could just go on living there inside the pickup's contented roar — gazing out across green cotton fields, across life as a living poem.

Later that day, as Sharlot sat barefooted on the front porch of the farmhouse and watched the sun going down, she began to have her late-afternoon thoughts. These were the ones that stayed buried and unobtrusive during the main part of the day, then rose inside her like small intimate balloons as soon as the sun sank below the telephone wires and everything on the farm began to still.

She remembered how as a child she used to sit on those same warped boards and think about Africa and being a missionary: about the long wide rivers she would travel, so brown and full of germs, and how she would stand in a little flat boat — straight and tall in a white missionary lady's dress — and how the natives would row beside her in tireless sweeps and the crocodiles would look at her with their cavernous eyes and the jungle and heat and sky would be stretching everywhere to the distance. She had wanted desperately to be a missionary, to go among far-away people and live in a simple hut in a clearing and teach the natives about God and His love.

As she sat on the porch and looked out across the yard and the flowers and the shadows lengthening beneath the humped mesquite trees, Sharlot was very glad that young girls who read a lot did not get their way about things. She was glad that on such a pleasant September afternoon she was not sitting in front of a hut in Africa but was right there on the familiar porch, listening to her mother in the kitchen make all her back-and-forth steps that were leading up to suppertime and hum over and over the same quavering fragment of a Baptist hymn. She was glad to hug her knees and watch the sun flood across the porch into the front-door screen — watch it move onto the living-room linoleum in a creeping triangle until it lay there like a huge yellow pennant celebrating the afternoon.

After the sun went down Sharlot walked around the house to the pens. She thought she would sit out on the fence with her Uncle Emmitt and watch her brother curry his calf. But a light coastal breeze was getting up and the sky was settling into twilight in the east — and as Sharlot sat there listening to her uncle and brother talk about cattle and the farm and cockfighting, and as she watched the big steady softening of the day, the feeling of sweetness and peace got so big inside her she couldn't stand it. To keep from bursting she had to go inside and help her mother with supper.

In college that fall Sharlot was lonely without knowing why. She dated some, as always; she got along well with the girls in her boarding house; she studied hard on her courses in Spanish literature. But something was missing — some deep little wedge that would make the puzzle of her life complete.

She had her job back at the library, and each night at closing time she stood at the inspection desk and gave her pleasant good-night smiles and nods to the students on their way out. Then when the library was finally empty she got her purse from beneath the check-out counter, shifted it to underneath her arm, and took one last look around the stacks and tables. Always, it was in that brief vacant instant, when her class and study and work routines were over for the day, that something in Sharlot seemed to crumple and die.

Putting her cheek against the coolness of the smooth library door — leaning there against it — she would start thinking again, with her eyes closed tightly against the thought: "There is never any change. Never. You keep hoping that just the passing of one more twenty-four hours will bring something, will have to bring something — and it always ends up the same. You keep believing that just one more day will bring something you can devote yourself to, something *meaningful*. But then that day ends too and here you are again with your face sticky against the wood, as though you really hadn't moved since the night before. And you'll go outside and it will be as if you had never moved from out there, either."

Sharlot would brush her wrist against the corners of her eyes and open the door and stand for a moment on the steps. There was the night, holding forth in all its old voluptuousness. The smooth college lawns lay in tinctures of moonlight, and long buildings loomed vaguely about. The same maddening black emptiness stretched everywhere.

The main library sidewalk was lined with tall palm trees, and at ten o'clock the limbs were crashing and tearing in the coastal wind, making furious sounds. As Sharlot passed by the palms they seemed like tall anguished mutes trying to burst into words, and she would have an urge to throw her arms around one of the trunks and cry out, "I understand . . . I'm one of you . . . I care." She wanted to hold on to the tree, hugging it until her wild loneliness had passed.

After she walked beyond the campus and got closer to her boarding house, Sharlot would become a little more at ease. The night seemed to lose its exotic hugeness; it was almost personal again, the way it was on the farm. Trees stood with a kind of sober friendliness along the sidewalks; fences had a tranquil innocence as they enclosed their shadowed yards. Even the sound of her footsteps gave her a sense of calmness and peace.

In her room on the second floor of the boarding house she would try to deal with the remaining hours before sleep by studying or sewing or washing her hair. But near midnight the full throb of her loneliness and despair would begin again. She would put down her book or half-finished dress and sprawl face down against the pillows of her bed, lying there under the glare of the ceiling bulb until she lost the heaviness of herself in crying or sleep.

That fall Sharlot came home frequently on weekends and took to driving down below the farm to the bay. It was pleasant there, especially toward dark on Saturday afternoons when Mexican families from nearby towns would be cooking supper along the shore and the smell of smoke from the camp-fires would mingle with the breeze off the bay. She liked to sit in her uncle's pickup and watch the small Mexican boys as they went racing by — chasing baseballs or each other, giving excited drifting yells to their friends far down the line of grassy dunes. Sometimes the boys stopped running and bent down to examine curiously shaped shells, or pressed their bare feet again and again into the dark wet shore, fascinated by the sand that quivered and sucked beneath their feet like a strange brown jelly.

Sharlot would leave the pickup and walk inland through a long mesquite thicket that stretched along the shore. By six-thirty the light was nearly gone and the air seemed worn out and depressed — as though exhausted by the weight of one more humid coastal afternoon. Once as she came out of the thicket into a stretch of open farmland, she saw that the sun was down behind a barn on the horizon — seeming to be covertly and serenely exploding there. The barn and other farm buildings were sharply outlined on the high rim of the land, while the green cotton fields that slanted down toward her were cast under a darkening hue. Standing there, watching the earth being gripped tighter and tighter in the intense sober spell of sundown, Sharlot felt old forgotten memories of childhood swirl about her. They were not about her family or — as far as she could tell — about herself; they seemed to deal only with trees and shadows and silence and grass. They kept surging through her until the last deep plunging moment before darkness came, then abruptly faded.

And once, just before cold weather set in, it rained on one of Sharlot's Saturday-afternoon walks at the bay. She had stopped on a grocery trip into town and was walking slowly, meditatively, through the dense mesquite thicket. The day had been full of heat and very sluggish, and clouds had been building in the Gulf since before noon. Sharlot noticed how heavily the birds moved along — almost seeming to swim in the air rather than fly. They stayed well below the level of the mesquite tops and never went very fast, looking bat-like among the vines and branches and shadows. A few old leg-horn hens from a nearby farm broke from their nests as Sharlot approached, careening wildly past her on off-level wings and running back toward the fields like small plump, armless boys. Once a mourning dove flew past her in a languid, drooping sail, as if exhausted from a sweaty afternoon of courting in the underbrush.

After a while the sky began to darken and there were hints of thunder in the east — peremptory at first, like someone coughing, or scraping back chairs in a large empty room. Soon more intimations came: long ponderous mumbles and echoes, buried high in the dark clouds. Finally, with the first clap of open thunder, lightning broke over the bay in a single, jagged, white-phosphorous line. More hens began running out of the thicket, and it was only after they had gone that Sharlot heard the deep quietness and realized all the birds had hushed or disappeared.

When she smelled the wind coming in hard and fresh, carrying the scent of rain before it, Sharlot started walking back toward the pickup. But before she reached it the water began coming down in driving sheets. Sharlot ran for a way, then stopped. She did not even bother to find protection among the mesquites; she stood in a clearing and let the rain cover and bathe and soak her. Rivulets of water ran into her eyes, filling and blinding them, and the sharp wind swept chill-bumps over her body. She looked up finally — in the direction she had always considered God's — and with her mouth stretched into the shape of a cry she asked of the tumbling, lowering blue-blackness: "What is life? What am I here for? Please tell me what You want me to *do*." But there was no answer that she could hear; the thunder just rolled more imperiously across the sky and her dress clung more wetly to her skin. So she stood in the clearing in the rain — dumbly, letting the rain fall on her without feeling it was either condemnation or mercy, letting it come down as it would on an ox or deer or any other creature of the land. And when it was over she walked back to the pickup and drove home.

Mrs. Bergman's Interlude

❧ MRS. BERGMAN, a stout, heavy-limbed woman, had worked dutifully hard in her lifetime at everything except developing a curious mind. She had raised seven children, nursed a bullying and cancerous husband until his death, and kept farm and household together with her plodding German will. But she seldom found herself arresting her dish towel in mid-swipe across a plate and stopping to say, "I wonder . . . I wish. . . ." Rarely did she speculate. She just never seemed to find the time.

Then one summer afternoon while she was gathering snap beans in her garden she fell and injured her back and found all the time she needed.

She had been moving along the fence, bending low to gather the beans in her apron, when she thought she heard a rattlesnake behind her. It was a dry and whirring sound, just like a rattler's, so Mrs. Bergman yelled "Mercy!" and threw up her hands and fell back hard between the rows. The beans, flung upward from her apron, came raining down on her face and for a moment seemed to be stinging like a whole den of rattlesnakes. Mrs. Bergman fought at them in blind terror as she struggled to get to her feet and run.

But she was trapped: she found that just rising to her elbows made the lower part of her back seem to come apart in a gigantic split and she had to collapse in agony against the ground. For a while she just lay suspended in her new world of shock and pain, forgetting the terror of the snake and thinking only of her back. When Mrs. Bergman did remember the little dry whirring sound, she gave a short scream and began scooting along on her rump and thighs toward the garden gate. Again the pain was unbearable and she was forced to lie still — her clawing fingers relaxing in the dirt.

At first she tried to catch the sound of a snake moving, but in the wide silence of the garden she could only hear blood pumping in her ears and a wild beating deep inside her body and, occasionally, the sound of traffic along the highway west of the house.

Lying there she thought: "My stars, I just *have* to move. I have to get to the house and phone. My back may be bad hurt — and Sharlot won't be in from school till five. I might lay here for hours. . . ."

While she was trying to think very hard about what she should do — thinking that if she could get to the gate maybe she could flop into the wheelbarrow and push herself along to the porch — she became aware of something else that was bothering her. Something was not right, was strange — and then she realized that her eyes were wide open and that she was staring straight up into the sun. She squeezed her eyes shut, but immediately a rattlesnake rose so hugely in the darkness of her mind that her eyes came flying open. She strained to look down her heaving breasts, tried to see the ground, and then once more tried to move. Whimpering and moaning, her body rainbowed a little as she raised her stomach high and slipped her hand beneath the small of her back, Mrs. Bergman slid backwards toward the gate — working her shoulders deep into the dirt and pulling her legs in sideways so they would fold underneath her thighs. But it was all too painful; a butcher knife seemed to be cutting into her back. She finally stopped her crawl, exhausted, and began to cry violently into the two-o'clock sun that kept on pouring down.

Afterwards, when the crying was done, everything around her was hot and moist. Dirt and tears and sweat were in her mouth. But her panic had drained away and now she just wanted to keep still a while. She didn't know whether she cared any more about the snake or not.

"Maybe it wasn't a snake at all," she thought." Maybe I just got my fool foot hung in a bean vine with some dry leaves on it, and then I pulled my foot away and it made a whirring kind of noise. Maybe that's all there was to it — just a little sound *I* made. And now here I've gone and maybe ruined myself, and over nothing. Ohhh, me — just a silly, excitable old woman, so big and awkward I break something just by sitting down. . . ."

It was while she was doing this natural sort of thing — scolding herself for being so jumpy and clumsy — that she found herself thinking a curious kind of thought, one that came from some forgotten place deep inside her. It didn't have anything to do with her pain in the garden, yet there it was, flashing past: "Why, I declare," the thought said, "this is the first time I can remember tasting *dirt* since I was a child."

The thought went away as quickly as it came and Mrs. Bergman forgot it — dismissed it as a piece of silliness. She had already put her mind back to business, telling herself: "I've *got* to move. I can't lay here all afternoon like this with maybe my back broke and maybe a rattlesnake around too. If I just lay perfectly quiet till I get me a little strength, maybe I can slide along an inch or two at a time, just taking it slow, and make it to the yard where somebody can *surely* see me from the road."

Having a plan to go by contented Mrs. Bergman a little, and after closing her eyes she tried to put her mind outside the garden, away from her pain and fear. She tried listening to things — the windmill turning by the gate, the sound of the icebox switching on inside the house. She even listened to the dog knocking his leg joint against the front porch floor as he scratched for fleas.

Gradually, without really knowing when she began, Mrs. Bergman found herself listening to the cars passing back and forth along the highway. As she listened she noticed that somehow the cars had a kind of pattern to them. Some seemed to be tied to a pair of very long pendulums, one swinging slowly toward her, the other swinging slowly away. Others were like the waves that always rolled in so peacefully down at the Gulf. Always before, cars had just been cars to Mrs. Bergman; she had never thought of them as clock pendulums or ocean waves. But lying there on the warm summer ground, with her eyes closed and her back throbbing and the sun pouring heavily upon her, Mrs. Bergman seemed to drift beyond the limits of her old self. It was as though she were some newborn child spirited out of her body and locked inside a warm incubator — where everything pulsed with blood and heat, where her mind found itself entertained by the sound of the windmill creaking and the pet lamb bleating and the stream of cars going by.

Some of the cars thundered past with a steady clattering, and Mrs. Bergman tried to imagine what the drivers were like. She supposed they were like the high-school boys that Sharlot dated in town: swaggering kids in dirty white polo shirts . . . grease on their arms from always fooling with motors and things. Somehow the cars sounded just like those boys always looked. Mrs. Bergman tried to puzzle out this curious notion, wondering how a car could really be like its driver.

There were more cars. Some were like slow-moving old

men, the kind Mrs. Bergman had seen pictures of: small, foreign-looking men wearing dark suits and small black hats. The cars seemed to purr along just like them, very well-mannered and neat. Mrs. Bergman could almost see spats and a cane as they motored past.

And there were trucks like the men who sang in the Baptist choir on Sunday — with that same heavy, serious roar. . . .

Sometimes the car waves stopped and a long silence fell on the highway. There was no traffic at all. Then, after a while, a very old and quiet car would proceed by at a moderate pace. It took its own good time in passing, as though finding a pleasure in showing off its smooth-working old valves. As it faded away — almost at the very moment that Mrs. Bergman stopped hearing it — a whole caravan of cars descended headlong on the moderate one's vanished sound: it was as if the cars had been dammed up somewhere on the road and had just now broken through. They were violent and fierce in their passing, as though holding the moderate one responsible for their long delay and determined to overtake it with a blaring of horns. But their excitement finally eased, and once again there was set up on the highway the familiar swish of the gradual approach and the humming fade.

For a long time Mrs. Bergman listened from her intimate throbbing prison, her mind feverishly playing with the sound of cars as it had never played with anything else in her sixty-three years of hard, conscientious living. And the longer she lay there, the more she found herself gradually thinking beyond the cars, beyond the sounds of the afternoon; her mind began edging itself into places it had never dreamed of going before. It seemed to Mrs. Bergman that if she kept on thinking and imagining for just a little while longer she would be on the verge of telling herself — well, she couldn't say for sure what, but it was bound to be important and revealing. For already she had told herself that if after living on the farm for more than thirty-five years and hearing cars by the thousands pass by day and night, she could suddenly start thinking about them the way she had just been doing — if she could suddenly change like *that* — then she was bound to start thinking a lot different about other things too. She told herself she was through being a donkey pulling the same old load — and never once looking up to see the Christmas tree. She knew that if she got out of the garden in one piece and wasn't crippled up by her fall, or snake-bit, she was going to start changing her ways if it just meant sitting out on the front porch in the afternoon and taking a little breeze and watching the world go by. Other women did that, and seemed to like it all right. She was through being an old German jenny. With only Sharlot left to see through school, she had a right to sit down in her rocking chair and get a little pleasure out of things.

Mrs. Bergman was right in the middle of all this long and involved speaking to herself when suddenly she remembered what *she* thought she would never be too busy or disabled to forget — what immediately became more important than an injured back or a snake in the garden or her unfolding creativity. And with her teeth clenched, and in great pain, she began to claw her way back to the garden fence, gathering strength all along the way from that womanly horror which was not only just hers but her mother's before her and perhaps that of all farm women everywhere: the fear of being brought into town from an accident and having the doctor she had known since childhood come into the emergency room to examine her with his white, scented, almost god-like hands and after turning her gently this way and that discover she was lying there, on his clean emergency bed, with dirty feet and dirty drawers.

The first few days after she was home from the hospital Mrs. Bergman sat dutifully on the front porch of her farm-house, listening to the afternoon cars passing by. She tried very hard to have original thoughts about them. She would notice a car approaching and would say to herself: "Now that car there . . . I'll watch it and see what it sounds like." And she would notice its shape and color and the noise it made and would follow it down the long stretch of road as far as she could see. Sometimes she would close her eyes and pretend that she was back in the garden in the hot sun, with sweat and pain and dirt all around. She would listen closely, trying to edge back into the secret cave of her imaginings and the once-strange procession of cars. But nothing ever seemed to happen. The cars she listened to did not change themselves into old men in gaiters or mousy women with shawls across their shoulders. They seemed to be just *cars* — exactly like all the others that had been passing by the farm for so many years.

Gradually — telling herself that she needed a little exercise — Mrs. Bergman took to leaving her rocking chair on the front porch and doing a little careful weeding in the garden. She always took a firm grip on her hoe just in case a real rattle-snake should ever make an appearance sometime. With her chest thrown forward unnaturally from the rigid curve of her brace, she worked up and down the rows, her strong arms making steady chops of the hoe into the weeds. She worked there each afternoon while cars went by in droves along the highway, and though she occasionally remembered to stop and consider them, they never once sounded like pendulums or ocean waves.

VI

Over the State

A Walk in Colored Town

❦ YOU WALK ALONG reddish, rocky streets on the east side of Austin, hunting for some unknown thing you need, like a salt-deficient sheep searching for a lick. What you see is poverty, watchful faces, whiskey bottles, weeds — yet strangely enough they satisfy. You wonder if they are part of what you came the many blocks to find. So you walk on, encountering other things — these:

the Rose of Sharon Baptist Church, with its blue neon sign and moulting dominecker hens resting under the sagging front porch.

backyards full of broken-soled shoes and tall ragweed and the smell of chicken manure and an old inner tube hanging over the crotch of a tree.

colored children playing football in the yards and streets with a stocking full of rocks: children that throw and laugh and jump in the air a little way and then wait and laugh some more as the clumsy knot sails back and forth in the dusty air.

smaller children, sitting in the bare front yards with their legs apart, sifting dirt through their fingers and smiling.

one lone boy sitting in his old tire-swing, slowly dragging

bare heels through the dirt and watching you pass, following you with his eyes, a contented finger resting halfway in his nose.

and continuously, street after street, old colored men with steel-rimmed glasses sitting on their porches behind morning glory vines; old men with their hats on who sit erect in their straight-backed chairs, holding their pipes out a little ways from them, not in acts of reflection but simply in peace; old men whom you sometimes don't actually see but instead perceive there in the porch dimness, silent and watchful of the street, the pipe smoke curling invisibly in front of them; old men whom you sometimes don't actually hear talking, either, but whose low words you can almost feel against your back as you move on by — old carved figures that represent a formidable and unique mixture of age and sitting and colored man.

Man in the Country

ON AN AFTERNOON of great and intense heat a man is on a road leading north from Waco. The heat is very strong, seeming to come down on the earth from the very heart of the sun. But the man, hatless, in short sleeves, walks easily along, smiling in a pleased way and gazing about him with a glad eye.

The houses become fewer as the blocks go by, and soon the man is by himself in the farmland. The road is silent and free of traffic, and even the summer insects seem stilled.

The man walks through it all — the heat, the heavy silence, the stretched-out land — and gives no sense of fatigue, even though sweat gathers on him everywhere.

It is June, and the fields underneath the sun are full of waist-high green crops that move like giant lazy grass whenever the wind comes by.

The man walks a long way into the country, evidently quite pleased with being out in the sun and being near the wide fields. The sun seems to be a strong, cleansing force that he welcomes, the way a steel knife might welcome the tempering blaze of a fire.

The man finally leaves the road and enters a nearby field. He wades patiently through the maze of blades, idly trailing his hands as he would in moving deeper into a pool of water or passing through the outstretched arms of many eager children.

When he reaches a point far out in the field he stops, and for a long time he stands there under the sky like a buoyed marker in a grass-green sea. Nothing happens — nothing beyond the same soft washing of wind against the growing corn, the same hard blazing of sun, the same tireless stretching out of the summertime land. But for a moment the man seems to find what he is looking for — perhaps some kind of communion or release — and he stands there in the brief intensity of it like a monument or tree, fusing himself into the earth.

The moment does not last long. The man stands gazing out across the horizon and then, very slowly, he begins to wade back out of the field toward the road. As he crawls over the wire fence his shirt shows dark circles of sweat underneath the arms, and his face looks flushed. He seems very tired now, and solemn, and as he walks back toward town he squints hard against the afternoon sun.

Blind Hillbilly Singers

🌑 SLOWLY THEY MOVED up Houston Street in San Antonio with their wide blue-white eyes. With one holding to the other's back pocket they sang in high, nasal voices, both faces turned slightly inward toward each other. One held a tin cup and made a small, steady, jangling rhythm with the coins and the other dropped his arm back and forth across the face of an old guitar.

That nose on one: a cucumber wrinkled in fierce dedication. And that mouth on the other: a crooning, wet, tush-filled cavern which had never seen itself in song — wholly unself-conscious, wholly intent on making its whining Tennessee sound.

Held together by the hand in the back pocket, they advanced block after block, mourning Old Shep Who Had Gone . . . Old Faithful . . . The Great Speckled Bird . . . The Old Rugged Cross. With each new jingle heard in the cup, they nodded together politely, in rhythm, dancing their eyes around like loose marbles but keeping their brows knit with strain.

They would stop between sets of songs and take out their cigarettes. Hands or arms would bump a little in the lighting, then there would be quiet, confidential smiles as they spoke together and rolled their whitish eyes. Occasionally one of them flattened his hand smoothly across his hair, as if he had just noticed that it needed combing.

Ben Milam Park

❦ ON LATE SATURDAY AFTERNOONS the Mexican men sat on the park benches along the sidewalk, legs crossed, arms folded, their eyes the only active things about them. The men sat looking out at the close of day, watching it draw into itself, watching it become gradually more intense as it neared its end. And before the men the paling sky arched over the high buildings of the San Antonio business district like a painted amphitheater of eggshell blue, making the world seem to be a very close and stable and comfortable thing.

The men looked at each newcomer who sat down on the benches, and in good time the newcomer would look around at them. Those who found they knew each other nodded and raised a hand or perhaps a single finger in brief salute. Sometimes the two of them would begin a little mild brand of talk — neither man looking at the other but instead simply joining in the gaze out toward the street. The men not involved in the talking would absorb the presence of the newcomer and his words without ever losing track of the street scenes before them or the slow passersby crossing the park. It was as if a code agreed to by the men required that a person who sat on the benches should always have his interests turned away from himself at the end of the day.

The men were not park idlers whiling away their last vacant moments before nightfall. They were just uncomplex and patient men who were responding in a quiet and respectful way to one of the timeless dramas of the earth. Men just off from their hours of work, they had come to sit in a place of grass and trees and watch once again how the day always brings its awesome business to a close: how another time of light is ended. They had just sought out a favorite place to rest and to watch it all.

Sitting there in their cement-splotched khakis and old greasy hats, they appeared ageless and durable and full of peace, as though they had succeeded in learning one vital and basic fact through the years: that no matter how many ulcers one might get by denying it, nature is first and men are second and it has always worked best this way.

. . . What a contrast there was between these peaceful men — who had come not only to watch and accept but also to celebrate the triumph of life's forces over their own — and Ben Milam standing a few yards away in the center of the park. He stood there on his granite pedestal, clenching his rifle and seeming to challenge the authority of the skies as night fell around him. He seemed to be making one last-ditch effort to rally the forces within the park — to wrest some sort of final victory out of the day for Man. "Hail man, not the universe . . . hail only him and his strivings!" — the cry was almost visible on his lips, futile words that would be covered by darkness in just a moment more. How strange and isolated he appeared there in his park just then, how alone in his vigor and protest: a final, upthrusting figure trying to stretch heavenward out of the passive ground, denying to the very end that he was of the earth and bound to it. ❧

Grudge

🌿 FRANCES LOGETTI, in all her thirty-three years, had never known a man to touch her — she had very thin legs and a rather large nose. Then one day during the World Series, Sam Wolford pressed her arm while they worked together at the filing cabinets of the Dallas First Federal Savings and Loan. Frances didn't let on that she noticed, of course. The sudden home run, the constant folksy crackle of the radio announcer, the general afternoon buoyancy in the office — any of these could have caused Sam's spontaneous gesture.

But there was a noticeable change in Frances after that. She came to the office wearing a black rinse on her hair that had prematurely grayed, and she took to dropping her eyes whenever Sam came near her desk. However, she might as well saved herself the trouble — nothing ever came of it. No matter how she switched her wardrobe about and dropped her eyes and rinsed her hair, Sam never seemed attracted. The following February he was promoted to a better job and moved into a different office.

Frances started telling herself that it certainly was a foolish kind of person who would take encouragement from a man just laying his hand on you during a World Series game. Nevertheless, within a short while she started a grudge a-gainst Sam. She never went into his new office, and once, when he came back to ask her to do a little special typing, she brusquely told him to try someone who wasn't busy.

The grudge was against Sam, against his violation of her rather peaceful old-maid's boredom, yet gradually Frances found herself using it as a wedge to force open talk about other grievances. During afternoon coffee breaks she surprised her girl friends with remarks like: "That damn janitor . . . he ought to be canned. You never see him but what he's off at the end of some hallway, smoking a cigarette and staring out a window." Or: "I guess you all noticed Bill Hanrahan's tie — the same red checked one four days in a row." Frances soon got a reputation for having a tart tongue, and the office gang set up arguments just to hear what she would say.

One day she happened to ride the same elevator with Sam Wolford. They rode in silence for a bit, then in a level, clear voice that everyone in the elevator could hear she said, "Well, things have been pretty quiet since you left — thank God." She got off at the next floor. Sam rode on up, shaking his head to a friend. "I don't know what got into *her*," he said, and left it at that.

And it was the best he could do. He couldn't be expected to know about women and hands and the World Series. ⦿

Fort Worthers

❦ CALL THEM SNOPSES, OKIES, down-and-outers — they exist many places, with many names. Along the coast, sitting on stools in the dark little beer joints of Rock Port and Aransas Pass, they are human barnacles clinging to quiet shores. In San Antonio — in down-at-the-mouth Harlandale — they are sandy-haired fathers who slouch into a Walgreen's drugstore on Sunday morning, cuffing pale-eyed little Anglo-Saxon sons across the cheek. In Odessa they are rawbony waitresses with eyes like vultures, voices like crows — women with dyed, ebony-black hair and the thick, puffy, dead-white skin of albino alligators.

They're everywhere, poor devils, but mainly they are in the underbelly of drab, dreary Fort Worth: they think it is their kind of town.

(For where does a man go if he finally decides to give up

his corn patch at Glen Rose, or backyard garage in Jacksboro, or maybe just his park bench in Cleburne? Hell, none of that fancy Dallas; and Houston's too far; and Waco . . . well, Waco, maybe, but there's not a whole lot going on over there. Besides, it's got to be a place to make some money *and* a place that feels like home.)

So it's settled before they even begin thinking about it. They throw down the hoe and the wrench and the bummed cigarette and tell the old woman to get the kids in the car and they all light out for Cowtown. It's not just a town anymore and there aren't many cows, but it's head-and-shoulders above any place else. The men make for the aircraft factories — adding one more car to the swelling sea of cars in the company parking lots; learning how to say General Dynamics, Convair, Ling-Temco-Vaught as casually as they once said Humble and Gulf. And the women — the string-waisted wives of ex-turkey farmers and cedar choppers — they fit right in too. They tie on white aprons or toreador pants and slide into the cafes and honky-tonks without even a second look. Tough as they come, never giving an inch, they pick their teeth and stare off into space over the cash register with the best of them: tired little islands of sour gossip and country twang.

Saturday Night Dance

۵ OUTSIDE IS THE WEST TEXAS DARKNESS — bigger and blacker and emptier than any darkness has the right to be. Inside is a Saturday night dance.

Call it Rob's Place, or The Hut, or The Highway Inn — it doesn't matter; such places are always the same in West Texas. The great dark dance floor is there, with tables scattered along the walls in red-checkered tablecloths. The string band is down at one end on a small stage, the players wearing elaborate Western dress. Quick-moving waitresses — like white-aproned bees pollinating their customers with spore-filled bottles of beer — constantly thread their way through the surges of laughter and talk and dancing bodies.

The night has reached eleven o'clock and Little Leon is singing again. A small wiry man in a big Stetson, he stands close to the microphone and sings, "Slowly, I'm Fallin'," a favorite Webb Pierce recording. It's a lonesome tune, and as the dancers glide and pump across the floor they know it to be another of Their Songs, the kind that describes the loves and disappointments of their lives exactly as they happened — the way they themselves would tell about them if they only could find the words. The more little Leon sings in his high mournful tenor, the more it seems to the dancing couples that they have at last died and gone to hillbilly heaven. They clutch one another in even greater embraces — the woman with her hand high and tight against her partner's neck, the man with his arm angled deep along a blue-jeaned hip and thigh — and they are satisfied that they hear the gospel and feel the glory.

But the tune finally ends, the spell breaks, and arm in arm the couples walk back to their tables. Perhaps for a short distance a head of hair rests gratefully, peacefully, against a broad shoulder, and the man's circling arm is content around

the warm, sweating waist. Then — like a tray of glasses being dashed to the floor — there are sudden bursts of laughter, and the heads pop erect and the circling arms fall away. For as the couples begin to rejoin their friends they find that the ritual of Table Hijinks is still in progress: ice cubes are still finding their way into shirt collars; gin bottles are still being knocked over; giggles and hoo-raws and shoulder slappings are still the lifeblood of dance-hall camaraderie. And as the dancers settle themselves before the familiar rows of beer cans and liquor bottles and ashtrays, the sweet-sad heaven of Webb Pierce fades into the surrounding night — replaced once again by the oh-so-solid earth of Rob's Place.

Dolores

WHERE ARE YOU NOW, Dolores Závala? Where are you residing within your small mouse-person, looking out into the world with your round mouse-eyes? For a mouse you really were, you know — back then, when I was supposed to be teaching you in school. You, a neat pet fondled with my grateful eyes as you lived, captive, in your mouse-house desk and looked out past small folded claw-like hands to the strange school-book words I would put on the board for you to puzzle at (oh, what I would have given to see those delicate, almost-invisible whiskers you undoubtedly had — to see, just once, how they waved gently about your mouth as you pursed it slowly into one of those secret, sharing smiles of yours).

Oh, dumb Dolores, dumb daily mouse: how you gladdened me with each small, covert, almost languid gesture. I would watch you stirring about in your desk with that artful and unobtrusive restlessness you had while searching for stray pencils on the floor, perhaps, or a book you knew you didn't have — a tamed, well-behaved mouse moving noiselessly a-gainst the restraints of your classroom cage.

And then, finally, the burden you found so unaccountably strange was over — school was out for another day — and you would go wait on the bus-stop corner with two or three of your semi-mouse friends. I saw you there most afternoons, your books gathered in carefully against your breast, the western sun lighting the pink fuzz of your sweater, and it was as though you were making a tentative comment toward be-coming human — not quite a full statement, but gaining. Then the bus would come and as you stepped forward to nudge with your books the arm of a companion, you would smile that final, open dimple-starred smile — and almost become a full-blown Girl, giving out with an almost heady Young Girl vigor.

Days — Phenomonal, Unheralded

W MORNING, MIDDAY, DUSK — familiar triumvirate: how often they are disregarded; how often they are left to themselves, unheeded, as if they possessed no beauty and intimated no glory.

For who among us is the caretaker of the day? Once night and its mystery is gone and the business of routine human living starts again — once the nine-o'clock rush is over and the school buses have discharged their last swarms of children and the last cars have vanished into the downtown parking lots — who turns his attention outward, to the land, to the bright hours? Who sees that the morning is not merely used a bit like a ripe orange and then discarded — the juice squeezed out and the hull left, for whatever it is worth, to straggling corps of women in housecoats and curlers who make brief forays to their backyard garbage cans? . . .

It is possible, of course, that a gardener or disenchanted office worker staring out his window will occasionally become aware of the day — will suddenly be caught up by the excitement of seeing great masses of greenery spread beneath the sun; or realize that if he wanted to he could walk right up to a fruit-tree sapling growing out of a lawn and—free of charge— touch the soft hanging leaves and the smooth young wood.

But even gardeners and office workers usually prefer to ignore the air and sun — ignore them, that is, until a weekend comes along, or a holiday. Then, look out: with what intensity and seriousness the day is pursued! Entire mornings are embraced in violent acts of boating or golf, whole afternoons in sun-tanning or mowing the lawn. The day becomes a serviceable thing, managed for practical ends.

Who, I ask, can still enjoy a day without putting it to some use? Who delights himself with the everyday phenomenons — ordinary ones wrought by the sun when it decides to mingle lazily with weeds and soil and rocks? Who is still so free, so vulnerable, that he can discover for himself what a day is really about: what the sky can offer with its canopy of warmth and light, what the grass and leaves are saying with their simple manifestations of primordial green fire? 　　　➣

Waiting Room

IT WAS LATE AFTERNOON and I was waiting in the railroad station to meet a friend. I had started reading an article in a magazine, killing time; but after a while I laid the magazine aside and sat there reveling in the building and its cathedral peace.

I listened as the voices of station employees filtered in from unseen passageways — pleasant, casual, contenting. I heard the shoes of slow old men passing over the tiles in a kind of muted, rhythmic litany. A typewriter pecked somewhere in an office, a train released its swish of steam far down the tracks, a janitor's broom knocked hollowly against the porcelain in the men's washroom. And subtly connecting them — all the muffled, echoing, unhurried sounds — were the smells of cleaning compounds and a faint, immemorial dust.

While I waited there, musing, very much at ease, a Negro woman with her three granddaughters took seats down the bench from me. The girls wore starched pink dresses and had their hair neatly plaited. At first, before they got restless, they remained solemn and quiet and looked around carefully at their surroundings: at the roof arcing high above, the big supporting beams, the wide slabs of white-tiled stairs going up to the second floor. But finally one of the girls began to scoot along on the bench — just to hear the noise that her bare thighs made against the smooth wood. Then the others began to slide, and to look at each other and giggle, until their grandmother was forced to raise her hand warningly and say in a loud whisper: "Shhh, *girls;* not here."

As the three granddaughters composed themselves again, and as figures from the entrances continued to move almost soundlessly by, I wondered what it was that seemed to affect us as we waited in the huge room. I looked at the high doors and walls, the great imperious dome: Was it sheer size that intimidated us, the sense of almost Olympian dignity? Yes, that seemed part of it — the natural awe a person has for physical majesty and grace. But for me there was something else too: a feeling that the waiting room was somehow a *good* place, a place that year after year had borne the constant touch of human beings and in the process had not been defiled. Whatever urge men have always had, in their emptiness, to scratch *Me* on the sides of monuments and on rest room walls — it was absent here. The waiting room seemed to touch something deep in the human spirit, making it bow to the simple elegance of silence and air and stone. 🐦

Caution: Senses at Work

WATCH A YELLOW WINDOW SHADE on a quiet spring afternoon. From within your room watch the shadows of trees ebb and flow upon it like fluid Japanese etchings.

Look outdoors at the white boards of a fence, and the white boards of a garage roof slanting down. They are bland as widely spread snow. They are out there under the hanging oak trees all afternoon long, not talking, not moving, existing so peacefully and surely that they almost imply that *you* inside the house are the lifeless thing, an echo hung in the still spring air.

Listen to cars going by outside on the street, and then wait — yes, there it is, that lone mid-afternoon plane going by. It never fails to be there at these moments when the earth seems to stand in its quietest mood: an unobtrusive background drone, a piece of stillness grabbed up from the afternoon and transformed into a simple little monotone. . . .

Listen more, and become aware of those other small things that exist in the middle distance of afternoon — those things that are never quite heard or seen until you accidentally focus on them: in the filling station down the street, that exquisite and gradual circling down of the hubcap to the concrete floor as the garageman changes a tire — and that accompanying *pronunciamento* of the tire tool as it is dropped ringingly at intervals; the vital bursts of quick single sounds outside your window as young sparrows cry out in the trees: little arrow-brisk, peremptory sounds, strung in the air like muted, over-excited telephone rings; that clock in the adjoining room, moving like a trotting horse gradually becoming a racing one, getting more and more out of control as you listen — as though hurried into greater and greater speed by the goad of the room's incessant silence. ⟫

An Excursion into Mr. Reade

✵ WE CAN BEGIN almost anywhere with Mr. Reade. Let's catch him at the movies. There he is, at the side, by himself. He's unmistakable, even in the dark. Hear his little strained "huh-um," that fast automatic clearing of the throat? And now watch how he handles what is for most of us the rather routine business of sitting. First, there are the legs: should they be kept crossed, or perhaps firmly straight down? Or how about buckling them under and sitting on them, yogi style? See, he tries each position for a while, finds it . . . what — unsuitable? uncomfortable? Who can say, except that it is all a matter of nerves — and indeed, what else *is* Mr. Reade than a matter of nerves? And arms: what shall they be: crossed, or a bit akimbo? Or, as a compromise, how about each hand gripping a knee?

You see, it doesn't really matter where we start our excursion — at his school, in a movie, at the zoo. Mr. Reade will be the same quiet, hoarse-voiced, throat-clearing, arms-akimbo young man in all places, staring out at the world from his body-prison with his unblinking, sometimes frightened eyes.

Mr. Reade — twenty-nine, unmarried, rather solidly built — directed the Davy Crockett Junior High School Band in San Antonio, Texas. Back in his college days in Iowa he had seriously considered the trumpet as a career and he would sit for long hours practicing, his feet squarely on the floor, his elbows out at proper angles. He would have looked very good had he gone on with his plans: perhaps a little too tense for supper-club combos but excellent with the serious Young School of a Kenton-type group or even the Cities Service Band of America. With his fine posture, his solid frame, the green-and-white trim-fitting Cities Service uniform, he could have stood up with the Trumpet Trio and made precisioned, biting flashes of sound.

Yet he found he did not want the trumpet as a career and lost faith in a traveling musician's life.

"Nuts!" he said quietly to himself one day, and ended up after graduation in the public schools.

As a teacher Mr. Reade was a good man and very kind and patient. But he was hard to get to know. His students and fellow-teachers considered him too formal and private. And besides, he had grown a small tufted reddish beard.

But we must get deeper than this into Mr. Reade. We must find the essence of the man. Is there some catch phrase, some easy summary that can focus our attention on the basics of Mr. Reade? Well, let's say this: Mr. Reade was, above everything else, a highly conscious man. There was no sluggishness in him. Awareness resided in him like a jeweler's polishing rag, and it kept shining the facets of his perceptions until they stood illumined in his mind like rows of quiet, glistening gems. But also he was a human chameleon, responding not to color changes but to every emotional nuance that touched his atmosphere. Thus, Mr. Reade had become over the years a very much ill-at-ease man, highly *self*-conscious, sensitized to himself and his surroundings the way a blind man is to the various surfaces of his room.

Mr. Reade, being not merely a charged set of wires and pulleys and controlling neurons but human flesh as well, had habits and tastes in addition to a high intelligence. But they too marked him and set him aside as a nineteenth-century man obligated to find a suitable niche in the modern jet age. He was — to cite examples — a $10.00-leatherbound-volume man surrounded by thirty-five-cent paperbacks; a Haydn-and-Beethoven man confronted on all sides by Fats Domino and Little Richard. He was an onion-soup, green-salad, and an hour-or-so-for-lunch man faced with swallowing the sixty-nine-cent Walgreen special. He was even a straight-razor-and-leather-strap man, in an electric-razor bathroom.

Mr. Reade became, then, a study in control, in self-discipline, and this is what made him tense. The constant rub of himself against the world — both surfaces greased by the clear light fluid of his awareness — caused Mr. Reade to stand before life as a knotted fist.

What was he obligated to control — his mind? that smoothly-operating machine? No, it obviously controlled him. It was his body, his public image, that he had to beware of.

His body was of a rather stout frame, giving no indication to a casual onlooker either of neurasthenic heightening or of animal grace. Mr. Reader knew this, had felt his body move awkwardly in tennis and basketball, had known that only its bulk had made it serviceable as a guard on the high-school football team. Mr. Reade, from a child, knew about bodies.

The head — what of *it*? Well, the body had been saddled with a rather grim one, a Java man's head, which, to the same casual onlooker, might seem more interesting for its construction than for its contents. It looked as though the skull's framework had been wire ribs covered with papier-maché. Then, apparently, rough freckled skin had been stretched tightly across the dried, protruding maché bones. Finally, both the top of the skull and the chin had been seeded with brownish-red hair. The top hairs, upon growing out, were trimmed off to make a flat field of skull-bristles. The chin ones, a poor crop, were allowed to remain in a straggling force.

Where, in such surroundings, did the consciousness of Mr. Reade greet the outer world? Where could one hope to find the soul of this complex young man?

In the eyes. Only the eyes were not subjected to the forces of Mr. Reade's control and discipline, and they seemed to stare out at the world like the images of two forgotten children locked high in some prison tower. They not only watched but seemed to listen, too, as if over the years the burden of alertness and concern had become so acute that they could not afford to trust the ears any more than they could the body. Sometimes, if the light was in them just right, they seemed like the eyes of a stallion locked in a barn who is constantly smelling smoke but has no possible way to escape if a fire should break out.

In the late fall of his first school year a thing happened to Mr. Reade, and it was all brought on by Delilah Barrera. Delilah was a shy Mexican girl who played second clarinet in the junior-high band. She always wore her black hair in a neat, bouncing ponytail, and her round serious Indian face was a truly happy moon when she smiled. She wore neat starched dresses, carried her clarinet home each night to practice, and always tried to please Mr. Reade.

At the first of school Delilah had been afraid of Mr. Reade and his small reddish beard. He never seemed to smile like the other teachers and he spoke so quietly and pronounced his words so surely that Delilah did not ever want to do a wrong thing in band and get Mr. Reade angry at her. Sometimes when he went through the sections and asked members to play a line from a march for him, Delilah's heart would beat so hard she could not get anything but squeaks from her clarinet. Mr. Reade would never scold her, but spoke to her quietly and kindly, and after a while she could make the notes come out as they should.

As the months passed Delilah began to be less afraid of Mr. Reade, and she looked back on that day in October when

Mr. Reade had said in his quiet, hoarse voice before band practice started, "Delilah, will you pass out the folders for me, please. I have to go upstairs to the office a moment." And Delilah, who had come in early and was getting out her clarinet, looked up at Mr. Reade out of her wildest, blackest, most nearly frightened eyes and managed a little dodging jerk of her head that meant yes. That had been the first day Delilah helped Mr. Reade, and thereafter he asked her to do occasional band-room tasks. But just arranging folders on the stands or chalking notices on the board did not seem all that she should do for Mr. Reade. Sometimes when he stood on the little wooden platform and looked out over the band with his almost *listening* eyes, Delilah felt that he was sad, somehow. She never told this to any of her girl friends because they would laugh at her; they did not understand Mr. Reade. But all that fall Delilah wondered what she could do for Mr. Reade that he would be indebted to her for — something big, something he would remember her for all the rest of his life.

It was during the Christmas holidays that Mr. Reade made a visit to the city zoo. He wore his green-and-red golf cap, dark sunglasses, and gray houndstooth coat. His small beard was shining wirily in the sun. He was, as always, monumentally ill at ease.

He walked slowly, stopping to study the signs on the cages and to review the genus of the animal or bird. He was somewhat pleased by the flamingos and a bit disgusted with the Australian wild dog.

When Mr. Reade came to the Bengal tiger, he paused and, with his arms crossed and one foot slightly forward, stood regarding the long body stretched out in the dimness of its cage. Many long moments passed — Mr. Reade watching the tiger, the tiger looking back at Mr. Reade. Neither of them made any noticeable movement or sound until Mr. Reade, with his little pronounced jerk of arms and shoulders, cleared his throat. It was an ordinary hawking sound, with no unusual embellishments, yet another zoo visitor strolling past the cage at this moment would have been so struck by it that he would have walked on down the way a piece and turned around sharply to stare. It would not be anything he could put his finger on exactly — just a rather stiff-figured young man in a golf cap and a small beard coughing in front of a cage. But there was, nevertheless, an extra dimension to the scene.

It was not like someone clearing his throat *before* a tiger: Mr. Reade definitely seemed to be clearing his throat *at* the tiger.

And, knowing Mr. Reade, perhaps he was. Perhaps he had suddenly felt violently embarrassed at having stood there so long, silently appraising the tiger in his cage, and, in typical Mr. Reade fashion, was trying somehow to make amends. Mr. Reade knew exactly how he would feel if *he* were in a cage and someone came up and stood with his arms folded and stared, uninvited, at *him*. So perhaps the throat clearing was a sudden act of attempted politeness, a lame but sincere acknowledgment of the tiger's presence.

Or perhaps Mr. Reade was embarrassed at suddenly realizing that he represented to the tiger the same sort of blank-faced baldly staring person who came by day after day to look in at the tiger as if it were some true curiosity or freak. There *he* was, Mr. Reade, with his arms folded critically and staring, as if he were like all the others who sauntered by, stopped, and thought idly, "Hump, damned *tiger*. . . ." And Mr. Reade was not thinking that at all. As a matter of fact, he had stood there and slowly realized how much he and the tiger were really alike, in many ways, locked in the circumstances of their lives.

Perhaps it was having such thoughts as these in mind and suddenly, impulsively, wanting simply to say hello to the tiger and greet it on equal terms, as one fellow-animal on earth greeting another, that caused Mr. Reade unconsciously to clear his throat and release himself.

But his thoughts could get no farther, for at that moment someone called out, "Hello, Mr. Reade!"

Mr. Reade turned, and there, in front of the cheetah, was Delilah Barrera. She had her hand raised just slightly to show that it was indeed she, Delilah, who had called.

"Good day, Delilah," said Mr. Reade in his stiff-sounding voice. "Zoos are good to come to on holidays. I'm glad you know about such places."

"Oh, I come to the zoo all the time, Mr. Reade," said Delilah. Suddenly she exclaimed, "And guess what: yesterday the hippopotamus had a baby! I bet you can't guess what it weighed!" Delilah was very excited that she had thought about the hippopotamus and could make Mr. Reade guess.

Now the approximate weight of a new-born hippopotamus was exactly the sort of thing that Mr. Reade would happen to know. He also knew how long the pregnancy period was and how much a grown hippo weighed.

But Mr. Reade held his chin and beard thoughtfully and said quietly, "Well, let me think. I shall say . . . two hundred pounds."

By now Delilah's pupils were so round and black and shining that it seemed they would have to pop from her eyes out of sheer buoyancy.

"Oh, *no*, Mr. Reade, not *near* so much. Not *near*. It weighed *sixty* pounds. Not *two hundred!*" And she ducked her head and tried to hide some of her laughter from Mr. Reade. She was very pleased at asking him and having him miss so far.

"Well, now," said Mr. Reade, clearing his throat, "I must

not be very good at hippos." He tried looking a while at the cheetah and so did Delilah. They were both suddenly self-conscious. "But I think there *is* something that I know," said Mr. Reade, and Delilah looked up a little more directly into his face. "I know that without much trouble we should be able to find ourselves a vinegaroon."

"A *what*, Mr. Reade?"

Mr. Reade held up his forefinger, cautioning Delilah to ask no further but to trust him and she would see. And together they walked, rather formally, with Mr. Reade leading and Delilah just a bit to the side and following, to the reptile garden and the vinegaroon.

So it was that Mr. Reade, the band director, after a period of fall gestation, found himself the following spring developing a tender place inside his heart for Delilah Barrera of the eighth grade. It was a quiet little feeling, much like a father's love, but it warmed him and made looking at her and her shy ways a pleasure.

Of course Delilah, in her wildest dreams, could not, did not, conceive that such a thing as love, in either its raw or transmuted form, could lie within the bosom of such a man as Mr. Reade. Mr. Reade was grown, a teacher, and these facts alone were enough to eliminate him from even the imagined role of paramour.

And true to this very incontestibility — of his *being* no one other than that formal public figure of himself — Mr. Reade contained his little pastel-colored feeling of love within him and merely stared out a little more awarely from his already most cognizant eyes. No stitch of propriety was dropped, and he continued to talk to Delilah that spring in his same kind and gentle way. But he ended up with torticollis.

If you don't happen to know about torticollis, the dictionary says it is "an affection causing twisting of the neck and an unnatural position of the head; wryneck." That was Delilah's big gift to Mr. Reade, for him to remember her by.

It was during the second semester that Raul Hernández transferred to Davy Crockett Junior High and enrolled in band. He had all the appealing features that Mexican boys can have — stocky build, thick black hair that glistened like bristles on a new paintbrush, good strong teeth, a ready wit. He played the trumpet with undeniable skill and by the end of April had captured the heart of Delilah Barrera.

The result, of course, was Mr. Reade's torticollis.

It came about slowly enough. Each day Mr. Reade came to his band class after lunch and there was no Delilah to pass out folders. Each day there was no Delilah to tell him how the grass got up her little baby brother's nose when she mowed the lawn or how she was paying out a set of encyclopedias by buying coupons at the Piggly Wiggly. No, there was no more early Delilah. She was outside by the drinking fountain with Raul. Sometimes there was even a late Delilah, and Mr. Reade had to send her and Raul to the principal's office for tardy slips.

Each day Mr. Reade dreaded to go to his after-lunch class and see his shy Delilah in her new lipstick and permanent wave. Each day he dreaded catching her making eyes at her trumpeter. Each day he felt more ashamed of his attitude: "You're the one who is behaving abnormally, not Delilah," he told himself.

Nevertheless, one Tuesday afternoon in late April Mr. Reade raised his baton to direct a Palestrina chorale, stole a glance at Delilah and saw her new jade earrings, and was seized with his torticollis. His head was drawn irresistibly toward his right shoulder, and his right shoulder rose to greet it. The muscles locked and Mr. Reade was left sitting on the platform stool with his baton raised and his head at a 45-degree angle.

"Excuse me," he said hoarsely to the class and made his way unsteadily from the room.

"It's all nerves, Mr. Reade," the psychiatrist told him. "You are too nervous for your own good. You read too many books. You should go to more ball games." And for ten days Mr. Reade lay in the hospital, taking insulin and orange juice and untying his nerves. He lay for long hours on his narrow bed, many times just at the borderline between consciousness and sleep. He rarely thought of Delilah. He rarely was able to think at all. But sometimes it seemed that he could see standing in the doorway a tiger dressed up as a nurse, staring in at him on his white-sheeted slab and periodically clearing its throat.   ⊃

ACKNOWLEDGEMENTS

Some of these sketches and stories appeared originally in *The Texas Observer*, *Southwest Review*, *Texas Quarterly*, *New Mexico Quarterly*, *Descant*, and *Southwesterner*, and they are reprinted with permission.

R01 0101 7115

71B 2660

71B 2660
NOV 10 '72 S

818
B666

BODE
TEXAS SKETCHBOOK
5.

R01 010

BODE

TEXA
OF
Y
B
TE
C

NOV 10 '72 SOF

8
Ind

HOUSTON PUBLIC LIBRARY
CENTRAL LIBRARY

This book may be kept for FOURTEEN DAYS.
With due notice, it may be renewed once
for the same period. A charge is made for
overdue books.

5-2-70-30M-1

DUP TXR